Flow charts for the

Term Service Contract

This contract should be used for the appointment of a supplier for a period of time to manage and provide a service

An NEC document

June 2005

OGC endorsement of NEC3

OGC advises public sector procurers that the form of contract used has to be selected according to the objectives of the project, aiming to satisfy the *Achieving Excellence in Construction* (AEC) principles.

This edition of the NEC (NEC3) complies fully with the AEC principles. OGC recommends the use of NEC3 by public sector construction procurers on their construction projects.

Office of Government Commerce

NEC is a division of Thomas Telford Ltd, which is a wholly owned subsidiary of the Institution of Civil Engineers (ICE), the owner and developer of the NEC.

The NEC is a family of standard contracts, each of which has these characteristics:

- Its use stimulates good management of the relationship between the two parties to the contract and, hence, of the work included in the contract.
- It can be used in a wide variety of commercial situations, for a wide variety of types of work and in any location.
- It is a clear and simple document – using language and a structure which are straightforward and easily understood.

NEC3 Term Service Contract is one of the NEC family and is consistent with all other NEC3 documents. Also available are the Term Service Contract Guidance Notes.

ISBN (complete box set) 0 7277 3382 6
ISBN (this document) 0 7277 3378 8
ISBN (Term Service Contract) 0 7277 3376 1
ISBN (Term Service Contract Guidance Notes) 0 7277 3377 X

First edition June 2005

Cover photo, Golden Jubilee Bridge, courtesy of City of Westminster

9 8 7 6 5 4 3 2 1

British Library Cataloguing in Publication Data for this publication is available from the British Library.

Typeset by Academic + Technical, Bristol

Printed and bound in Great Britain by Bell & Bain Limited, Glasgow, UK

CONTENTS

The number of each flow chart is the same as the number of the clause in the NEC Term Service Contract to which it primarily relates.

Preface				v
Acknowledgements				vii
Abbreviations				viii
Legend				1
Flow charts	13	Communications	Sheets 1 to 3	3
	14	The *Service Manager*		6
	15	*Employer* provides right of access and things		7
	16	Early warning		8
	17	Ambiguities and inconsistencies		9
	18	Illegal and impossible requirements		10
	20	Providing the Service		11
	21	The *Contractor*'s plan	Sheets 1 and 2	12
	22	Revising the *Contractor*'s plan		14
	23	Design of Equipment		15
	25	Working with the *Employer* and Others		16
	26	Subcontracting	Sheets 1 and 2	17
	27	Other (*Contractor*) responsibilities		19
	30	Starting and the *service period*		20
	31	Access		21
	32	Instructions to stop or not to start work		22
	40	Tests and inspections	Sheets 1 and 2	23
	41	Testing and inspection before delivery		25
	42	Correcting Defects		26
	43	Accepting Defects		27
	50	Assessing the amount due	Sheets 1 to 6	28
	51	Payment	Sheets 1 and 2	34
	52	Defined Cost		36
	53	The *Contractor*'s share (Option C)		37
	54	Price List		38
	60	Compensation events	Sheets 1 to 6	39
	61	Notifying compensation events	Sheets 1 to 3	45
	62	Quotations for compensation events	Sheets 1 and 2	48
	63	Assessing compensation events	Sheets 1 to 3	50
	64	The *Service Manager*'s assessments	Sheets 1 and 2	53
	65	Implementing compensation events		55
	70	The Parties' use of equipment, Plant and Materials		56
	80	*Employer*'s risks	Sheets 1 to 3	57
	81	*Contractor*'s risks		60
	82	Indemnity		61
	83	Insurance cover		62
	84	Insurance policies		63
	85	If the *Contractor* does not insure		64
	86	Insurance by the *Employer*		65
	90	Termination		66
	91	Reasons for termination	Sheets 1 to 5	67
	92	Procedures on termination		72
	93	Payment on termination		73
	W1	Dispute resolution procedure W1	Sheets 1 to 5	74
	W2	Dispute resolution procedure W2	Sheets 1 to 6	79
	X1	Price adjustment for inflation (used only with Options A and C)		85

X2	Changes in the law		86
X3	Multiple currencies (used only with Option A)		87
X4	Parent company guarantee		88
X12	Partnering	Sheets 1 to 3	89
X13	Performance bond		92
X17	Low service damages		93
X18	Limitation of liability		94
X19	Task Order	Sheets 1 to 8	95
X20	Key Performance Indicators (not used with Option X12)		103
Y(UK)2	The Housing Grants, Construction and Regeneration Act 1996		104
Y(UK)3	The Contracts (Rights of Third Parties) Act 1999		105

PREFACE

These flow charts depict the procedures followed when using the NEC3 Term Service Contract (TSC). They are intended to help people using the TSC to see how the various TSC core clauses and Options come together to produce clear and precise sequences of action for the people involved.

The flow charts are not part of any contract. Much of the text and many of the words taken from the TSC itself are abbreviated in the flow charts. The flow charts depict almost all of the sequences of action set out in the TSC. Many of the sequences interact and, therefore, users of the flow charts will often have to review more than one sheet in order to track the full sequence of actions in one area.

ACKNOWLEDGEMENTS

The first edition of the NEC3 Term Service Contract was drafted by the Institution of Civil Engineers NEC Panel through its Term Service Contract Working Group whose members were:

P. A. Baird, BSc, CEng, FICE, M(SA)ICE, MAPM
M. Barnes, BSc(Eng), PhD, FREng, FICE, FCIOB, CCMI, ACIArb, MBCS, FInstCES, FAPM
T. W. Weddell, BSc, CEng, DIC, FICE, FIStructE, ACIArb

The Flow Charts were produced by Ross Hayes with assistance from Tom Nicholson.

The original NEC was designed and drafted by Dr Martin Barnes then of Coopers and Lybrand with the assistance of Professor J. G. Perry then of the University of Birmingham, T. W. Weddell then of Travers Morgan Management, T. H. Nicholson, Consultant to the Institution of Civil Engineers, A. Norman then of the University of Manchester Institute of Science and Technology and P. A. Baird, then Corporate Contracts Consultant, Eskom, South Africa.

The members of the NEC Panel are:

P. Higgins, BSc, CEng, FICE, FCIArb (Chairman)
P. A. Baird, BSc, CEng, FICE, M(SA)ICE, MAPM
M. Barnes, BSc(Eng), PhD, FREng, FICE, FCIOB, CCMI, ACIArb, MBCS, FInstCES, FAPM
A. J. Bates, FRICS, MInstCES
A. J. M. Blackler, BA, LLB(Cantab), MCIArb
P. T. Cousins, BEng(Tech), DipArb, CEng, MICE, MCIArb, MCMI
L. T. Eames, BSc, FRICS, FCIOB
F. Forward, BA(Hons), DipArch, MSc(Const Law), RIBA, FCIArb
Professor J. G. Perry, MEng, PhD, CEng, FICE, MAPM
N. C. Shaw, FCIPS, CEng, MIMechE
T. W. Weddell, BSc, CEng, DIC, FICE, FIStructE, ACIArb

NEC Consultant:

R. A. Gerrard, BSc(Hons), MRICS, FCIArb, FInstCES

Secretariat:

A. Cole, LLB, LLM, BL
J. M. Hawkins, BA(Hons), MSc
F. N. Vernon (Technical Adviser), BSc, CEng, MICE

ABBREVIATIONS USED IN THE FLOW CHART BOXES

FC 61	Flow chart for clause 61
FC X2	Flowchart for secondary Option X2
E	*Employer*
C	*Contractor*
SM	*Service Manager*
SC	Subcontractor
CD	Contract Data
CE	Compensation event
P&M	Plant and Materials
PAF	Price Adjustment Factor
PSPD	Price for Services Provided to Date
SI	Service Information

Legend

CHART START

HEADINGS
    Headings in caps
    provide guidance

STATEMENTS
    If a subclause is
    referenced, text
    is from the NEC

LOGIC LINKS
    Links go to right
    and/or downward
    unless shown

QUESTION
    Answer question
    to determine the
    route to follow

SUBROUTINE
    Include another
    flow chart here

CONTINUATION
    Link to matching
    point(s) on other
    chart sheets

CHART TITLE
    Chart number,
    title and sheet

Start

HELPFUL HEADING

Statement explaining next step

Subclause or
Statement using part or all of the NEC text in subclause

Does this subclause apply? YES NO

FC or Description

A sheet 2

B sheet 2

Flow chart or Sheet 1 of 2
Description

CONTINUATION

A sheet 2

B sheet 2

CHART FINISH

Finish

CHART TITLE

Flow chart or Sheet 2 of 2
Description

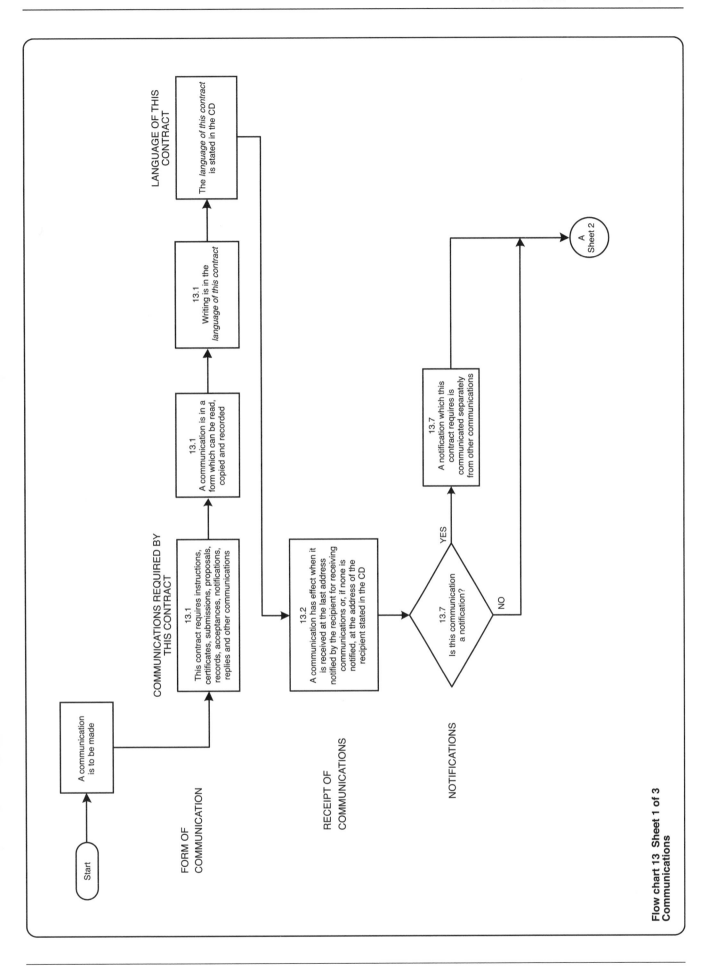

FORM OF
COMMUNICATION

RECEIPT OF
COMMUNICATIONS

NOTIFICATIONS

Flow chart 13   Sheet 1 of 3
Communications

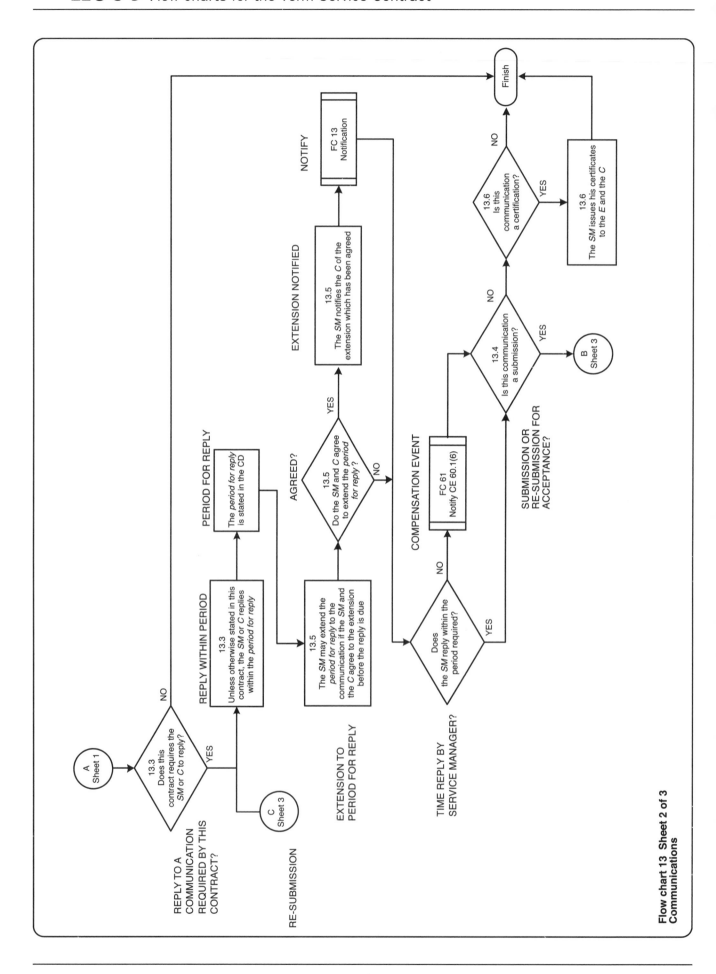

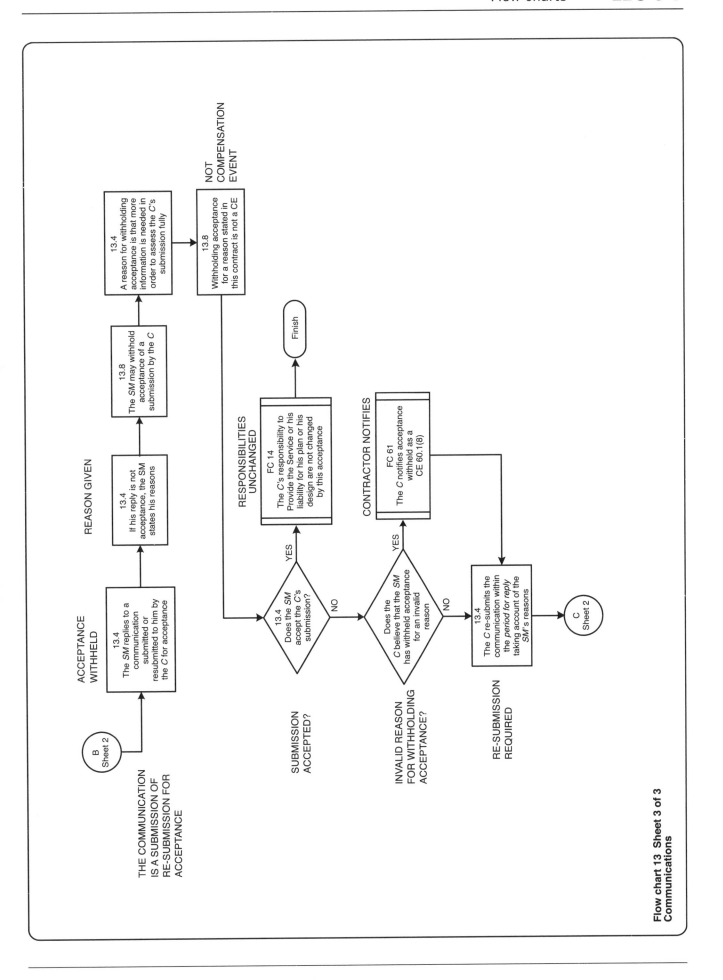

THE COMMUNICATION
IS A SUBMISSION OF
RE-SUBMISSION FOR
ACCEPTANCE

ACCEPTANCE
WITHHELD

REASON GIVEN

NOT
COMPENSATION
EVENT

B
Sheet 2

13.4
The *SM* replies to a
communication
submitted or
resubmitted to him by
the *C* for acceptance

13.4
If his reply is not
acceptance, the SM
states his reasons

13.8
The *SM* may withhold
acceptance of a
submission by the *C*

13.4
A reason for withholding
acceptance is that more
information is needed in
order to assess the *C*'s
submission fully

13.8
Withholding acceptance
for a reason stated in
this contract is not a CE

SUBMISSION
ACCEPTED?

13.4
Does the *SM*
accept the *C*'s
submission?

YES

NO

RESPONSIBILITIES
UNCHANGED

FC 14
The *C*'s responsibility to
Provide the Service or his
liability for his plan or his
design are not changed
by this acceptance

Finish

INVALID REASON
FOR WITHHOLDING
ACCEPTANCE?

Does the
C believe that the *SM*
has withheld acceptance
for an invalid
reason

YES

NO

CONTRACTOR NOTIFIES

FC 61
The *C* notifies acceptance
withheld as a
CE 60.1(8)

RE-SUBMISSION
REQUIRED

13.4
The *C* re-submits the
communication within
the *period for reply*
taking account of the
SM's reasons

C
Sheet 2

Flow chart 13   Sheet 3 of 3
Communications

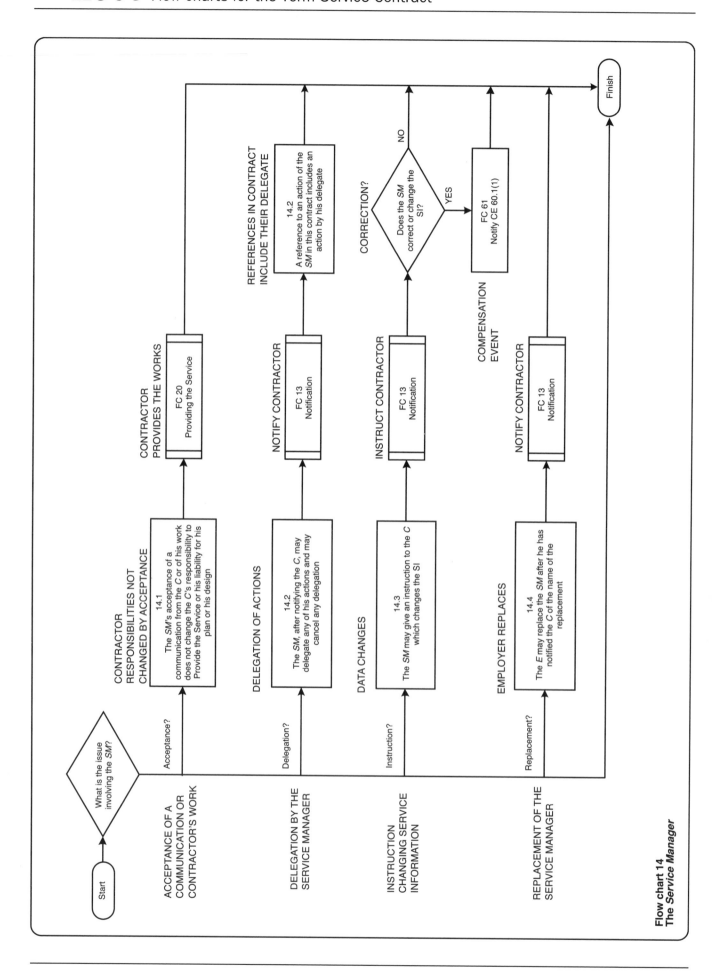

Start

What is the issue involving the *SM*?

Acceptance? → **ACCEPTANCE OF A COMMUNICATION OR CONTRACTOR'S WORK**

CONTRACTOR RESPONSIBILITIES NOT CHANGED BY ACCEPTANCE
14.1
The *SM's* acceptance of a communication from the *C* or of his work does not change the *C's* responsibility to Provide the Service or his liability for his plan or his design

CONTRACTOR PROVIDES THE WORKS
FC 20
Providing the Service

Delegation? → **DELEGATION BY THE SERVICE MANAGER**

DELEGATION OF ACTIONS
14.2
The *SM*, after notifying the *C*, may delegate any of his actions and may cancel any delegation

NOTIFY CONTRACTOR
FC 13
Notification

REFERENCES IN CONTRACT INCLUDE THEIR DELEGATE
14.2
A reference to an action of the *SM* in this contract includes an action by his delegate

Instruction? → **INSTRUCTION CHANGING SERVICE INFORMATION**

DATA CHANGES
14.3
The *SM* may give an instruction to the *C* which changes the SI

INSTRUCT CONTRACTOR
FC 13
Notification

CORRECTION?
Does the *SM* correct or change the SI?
NO
YES

Replacement? → **REPLACEMENT OF THE SERVICE MANAGER**

EMPLOYER REPLACES
14.4
The *E* may replace the *SM* after he has notified the *C* of the name of the replacement

NOTIFY CONTRACTOR
FC 13
Notification

COMPENSATION EVENT
FC 61
Notify CE 60.1(1)

Finish

Flow chart 14
The *Service Manager*

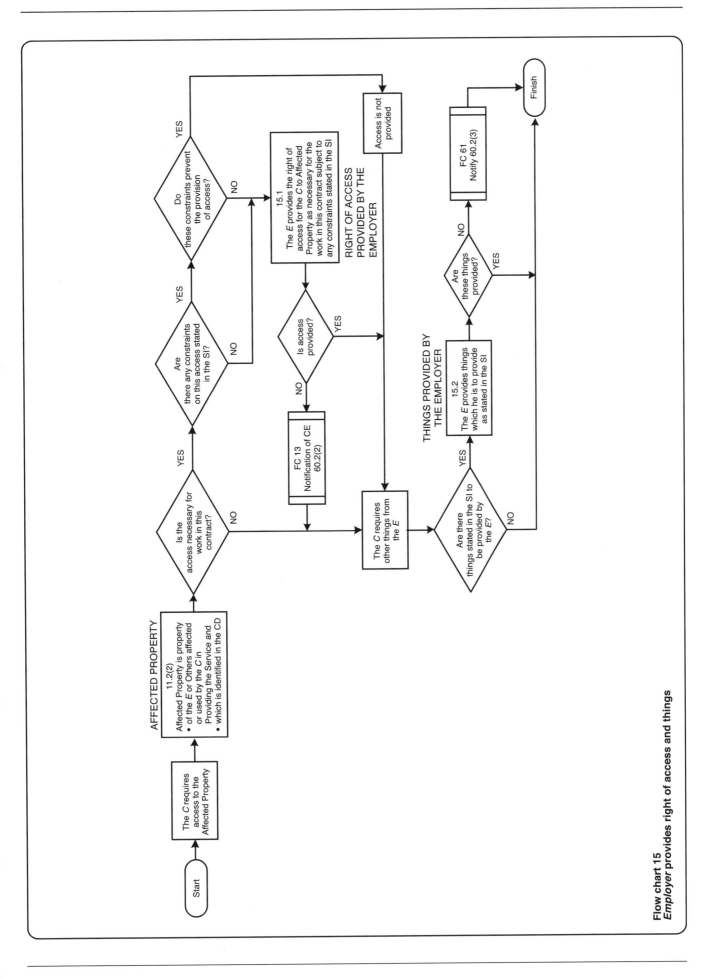

Flow chart 15
Employer **provides right of access and things**

Start

16.1
The C and the SM give an early warning by notifying the other as soon as either becomes aware of any matter which could
- increase the total of the Prices,
- interfere with the timing of the service or
- impair the effectiveness of the service

16.1
The C may give an early warning by notifying the SM of any other matter which could increase his total cost

16.1
Does such a notifiable matter occur?
NO / YES

16.1
Has a CE already been notified
YES / NO

16.1
Early warning of a matter for which a CE has previously been notified is not required

COMPENSATION EVENT NOTIFIED

FC 13
Notification

16.2
Either the SM or the C may instruct the other to attend a risk reduction meeting

16.2
Is a risk reduction meeting instructed?
NO / YES

INSTRUCTED?

RISK REDUCTION MEETING

OTHERS MAY BE INSTRUCTED TO ATTEND

27.3
The C obeys an instruction which is in accordance with its contract and is given to him by the SM

16.2
Does the SM wish to instruct other people to attend?
YES / NO

16.2
Does the C agree to those other people attending?
YES / NO

16.2
The SM may instruct those other people to attend

16.2
Does the C wish to instruct other people to attend?
YES / NO

16.2
Does the SM agree to those other people attending?
YES / NO

16.2
The C may instruct those other people to attend

16.2
A risk reduction meeting is held

THE PARTIES CO-OPERATE TO RESOLVE THE MATTER

16.3
At a risk reduction meeting those who attend co-operate in
- making and considering proposals for how the effect of the registered risks can be avoided or reduced,
- seeking solutions that will bring advantage to all those who will be affected,
- deciding upon actions which will be taken and who, in accordance with this contract, will take them and
- deciding which risks have now been avoided or have passed and can be removed from the Risk Register

PROPOSALS AND DECISIONS

16.4
The SM revises the Risk Register to record the decisions made at each risk reduction meeting and issues the revised Risk Register to the C

16.4
If a decision needs a change to the SI, the SM instructs the change at the same time as he issues the revised Risk Register

Does the decision need a change to the SI?
YES / NO

SM's INSTRUCTION

FC 13
SM's Instruction

Finish

**Flow chart 16
Early warning**

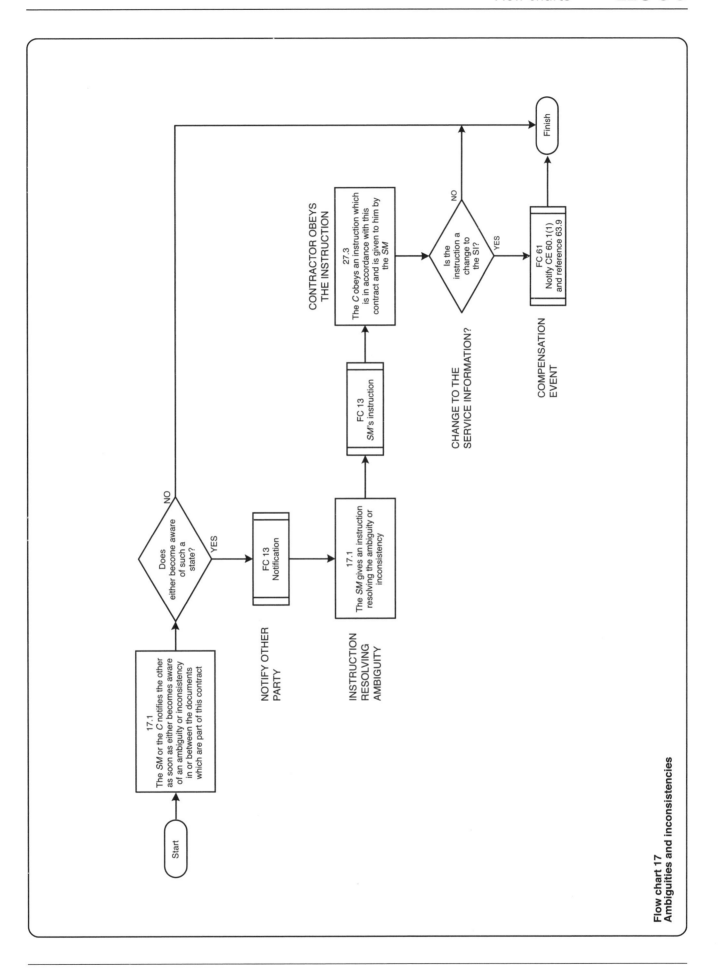

Start

17.1
The *SM* or the *C* notifies the other as soon as either becomes aware of an ambiguity or inconsistency in or between the documents which are part of this contract

Does either become aware of such a state?

NO

YES

FC 13
Notification

NOTIFY OTHER PARTY

17.1
The *SM* gives an instruction resolving the ambiguity or inconsistency

INSTRUCTION RESOLVING AMBIGUITY

FC 13
SM's instruction

27.3
The *C* obeys an instruction which is in accordance with this contract and is given to him by the *SM*

CONTRACTOR OBEYS THE INSTRUCTION

Is the instruction a change to the SI?

NO

YES

CHANGE TO THE SERVICE INFORMATION?

FC 61
Notify CE 60.1(1) and reference 63.9

COMPENSATION EVENT

Finish

Flow chart 17
Ambiguities and inconsistencies

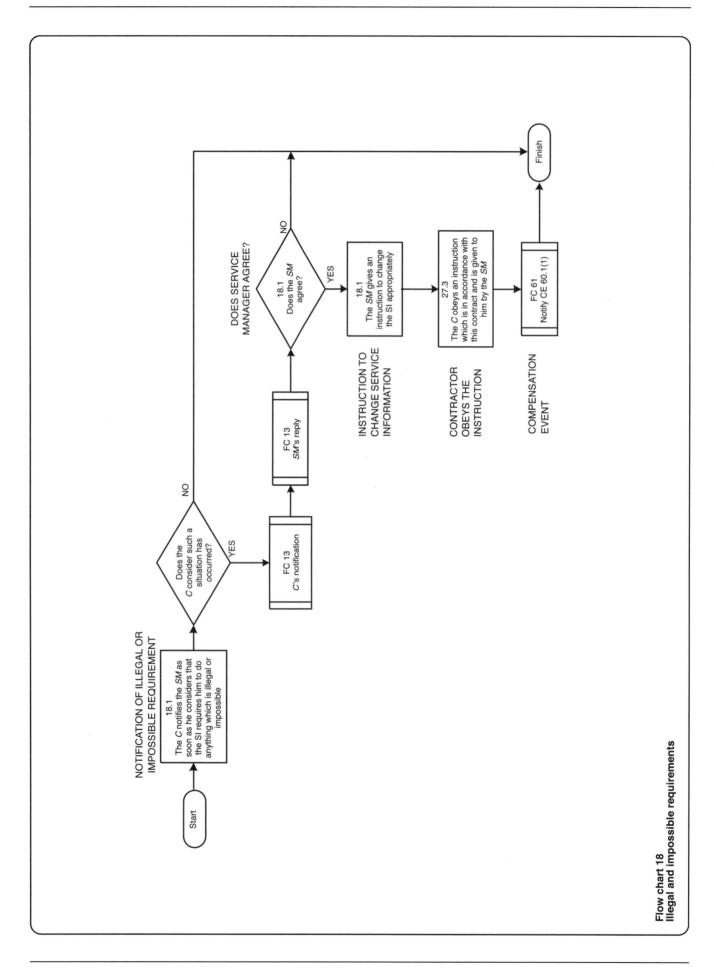

Flow chart 18
Illegal and impossible requirements

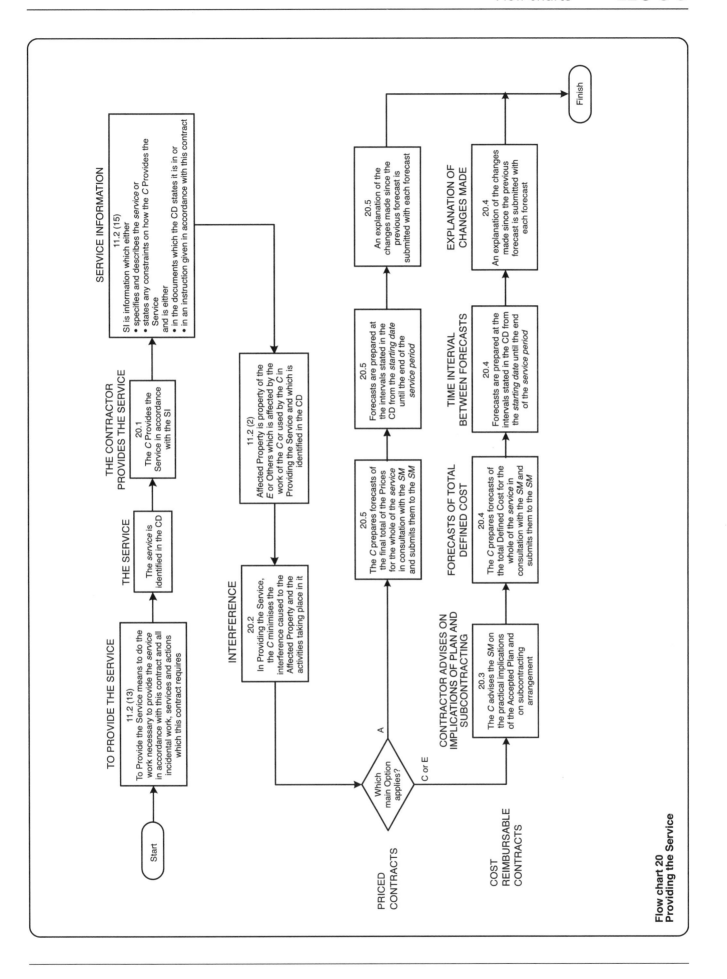

TO PROVIDE THE SERVICE

11.2 (13)
To Provide the Service means to do the work necessary to provide the *service* in accordance with this contract and all incidental work, services and actions which this contract requires

THE SERVICE

The *service* is identified in the CD

THE CONTRACTOR PROVIDES THE SERVICE

20.1
The *C* Provides the Service in accordance with the SI

SERVICE INFORMATION

11.2 (15)
SI is information which either
• specifies and describes the *service* or
• states any constraints on how the *C* Provides the Service
and is either
• in the documents which the CD states it is in or
• in an instruction given in accordance with this contract

INTERFERENCE

20.2
In Providing the Service, the *C* minimises the interference caused to the Affected Property and the activities taking place in it

11.2 (2)
Affected Property is property of the *E* or Others which is affected by the work of the *C* or used by the *C* in Providing the Service and which is identified in the CD

Which main Option applies?

A

C or E

PRICED CONTRACTS

20.5
The *C* prepares forecasts of the final total of the Prices for the whole of the *service* in consultation with the *SM* and submits them to the *SM*

20.5
Forecasts are prepared at the intervals stated in the CD from the *starting date* until the end of the *service period*

20.5
An explanation of the changes made since the previous forecast is submitted with each forecast

COST REIMBURSABLE CONTRACTS

CONTRACTOR ADVISES ON IMPLICATIONS OF PLAN AND SUBCONTRACTING

20.3
The *C* advises the *SM* on the practical implications of the Accepted Plan and on subcontracting arrangement

FORECASTS OF TOTAL DEFINED COST

20.4
The *C* prepares forecasts of the total Defined Cost for the whole of the *service* in consultation with the *SM* and submits them to the *SM*

TIME INTERVAL BETWEEN FORECASTS

20.4
Forecasts are prepared at the intervals stated in the CD from the *starting date* until the end of the *service period*

EXPLANATION OF CHANGES MADE

20.4
An explanation of the changes made since the previous forecast is submitted with each forecast

Start

Finish

Flow chart 20
Providing the Service

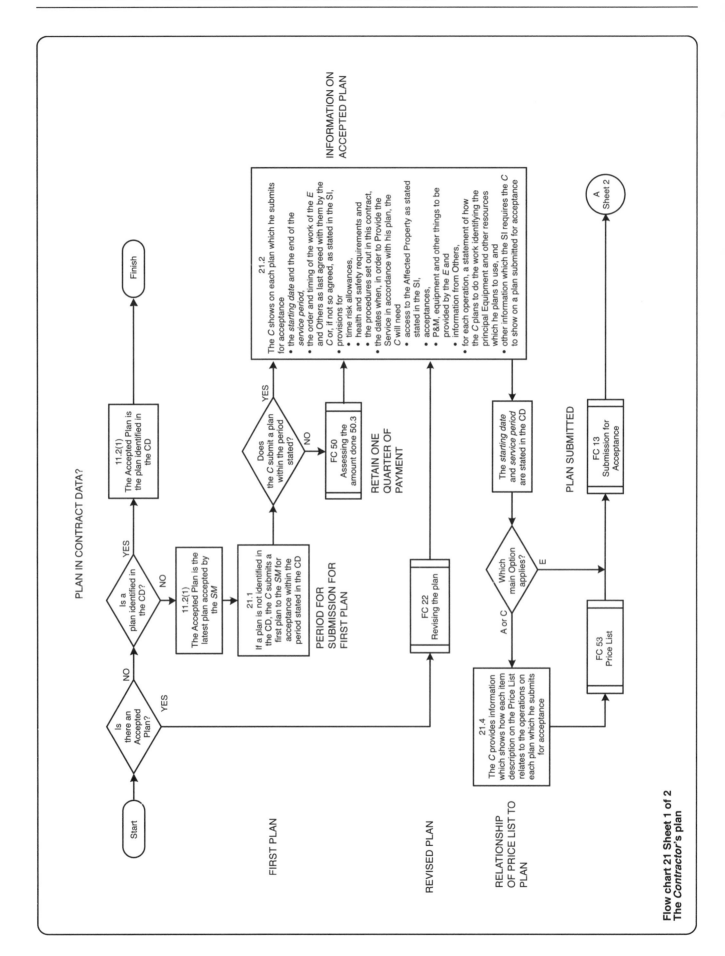

Flow chart 21 Sheet 1 of 2
The *Contractor*'s plan

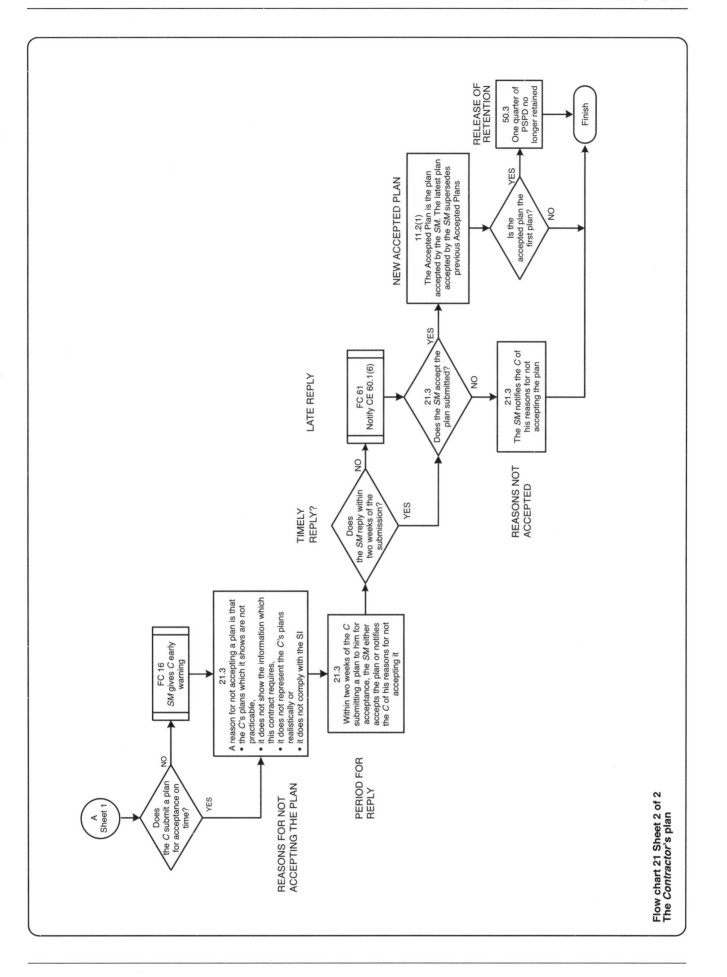

REASONS FOR NOT
ACCEPTING THE PLAN

PERIOD FOR
REPLY

TIMELY
REPLY?

LATE REPLY

NEW ACCEPTED PLAN

REASONS NOT
ACCEPTED

RELEASE OF
RETENTION

A
Sheet 1

Does
the C submit a plan
for acceptance on
time?

NO

YES

FC 16
SM gives *C* early
warning

21.3
A reason for not accepting a plan is that
• the *C*'s plans which it shows are not
  practicable,
• it does not show the information which
  this contract requires,
• it does not represent the *C*'s plans
  realistically or
• it does not comply with the SI

21.3
Within two weeks of the *C*
submitting a plan to him for
acceptance, the *SM* either
accepts the plan or notifies
the *C* of his reasons for not
accepting it

Does
the *SM* reply within
two weeks of the
submission?

YES

NO

FC 61
Notify CE 60.1(6)

21.3
Does the *SM* accept the
plan submitted?

YES

NO

21.3
The *SM* notifies the *C* of
his reasons for not
accepting the plan

11.2(1)
The Accepted Plan is the plan
accepted by the *SM*. The latest plan
accepted by the *SM* supersedes
previous Accepted Plans

Is the
accepted plan the
first plan?

YES

NO

50.3
One quarter of
PSPD no
longer retained

Finish

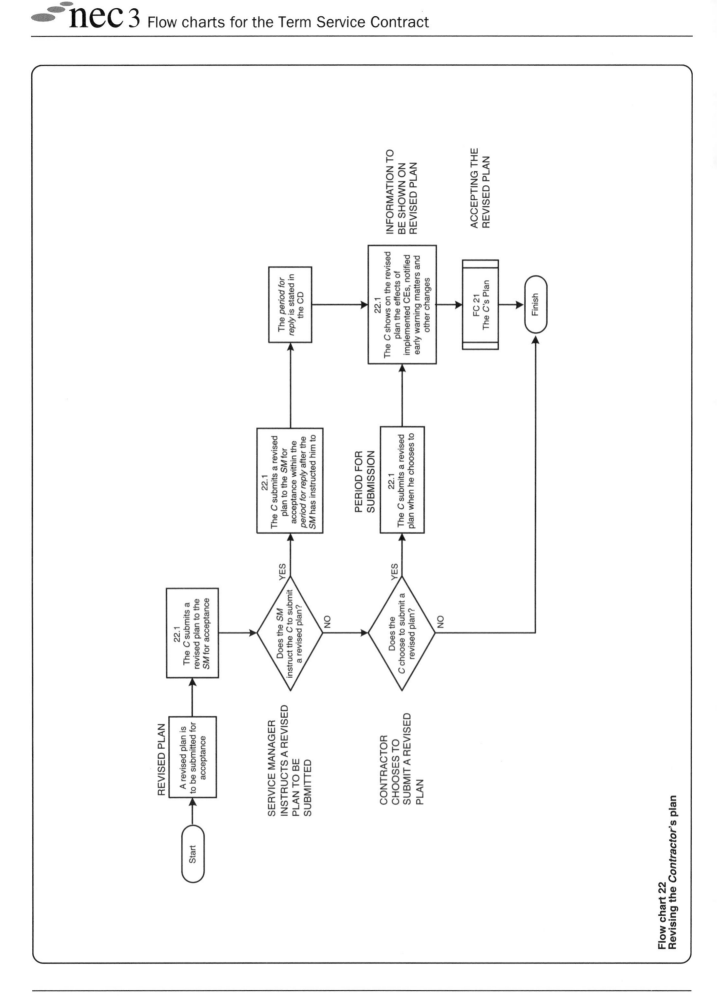

REVISED PLAN

Start

A revised plan is to be submitted for acceptance

22.1
The C submits a revised plan to the SM for acceptance

SERVICE MANAGER INSTRUCTS A REVISED PLAN TO BE SUBMITTED

Does the SM instruct the C to submit a revised plan?

YES

NO

22.1
The C submits a revised plan to the SM for acceptance within the period for reply after the SM has instructed him to

The period for reply is stated in the CD

CONTRACTOR CHOOSES TO SUBMIT A REVISED PLAN

Does the C choose to submit a revised plan?

YES

NO

22.1
The C submits a revised plan when he chooses to

PERIOD FOR SUBMISSION

22.1
The C shows on the revised plan the effects of implemented CEs, notified early warning matters and other changes

INFORMATION TO BE SHOWN ON REVISED PLAN

FC 21
The C's Plan

ACCEPTING THE REVISED PLAN

Finish

Flow chart 22
Revising the Contractor's plan

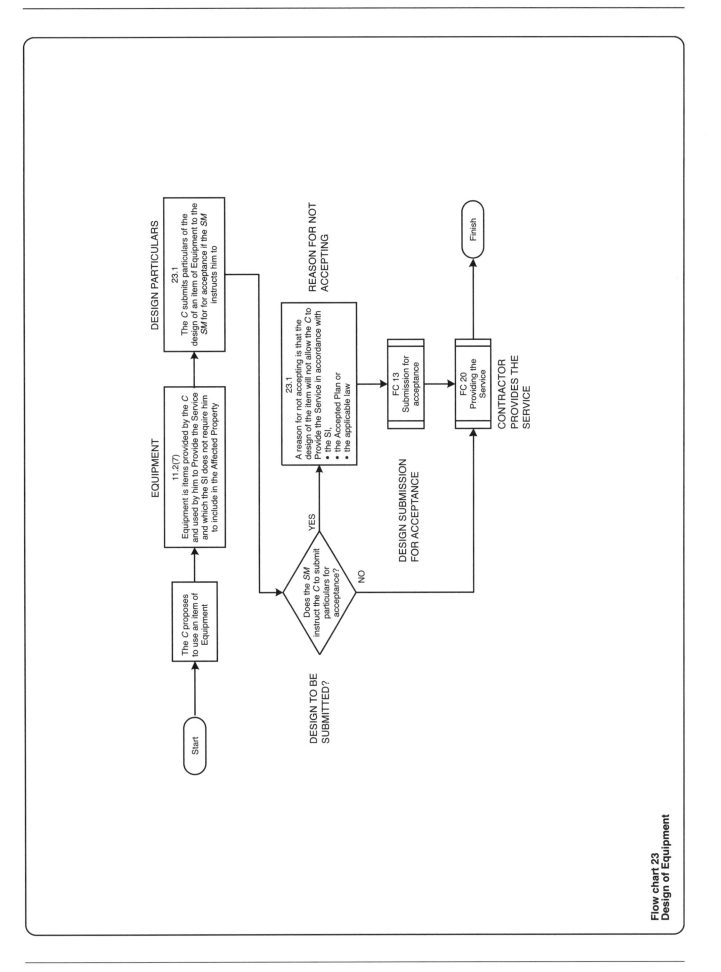

EQUIPMENT

DESIGN PARTICULARS

REASON FOR NOT ACCEPTING

Start

The C proposes to use an item of Equipment

11.2(7)
Equipment is items provided by the C and used by him to Provide the Service and which the SI does not require him to include in the Affected Property

23.1
The C submits particulars of the design of an item of Equipment to the SM for acceptance if the SM instructs him to

DESIGN TO BE SUBMITTED?

Does the SM instruct the C to submit particulars for acceptance?

YES

NO

23.1
A reason for not accepting is that the design of the item will not allow the C to Provide the Service in accordance with
• the SI,
• the Accepted Plan or
• the applicable law

DESIGN SUBMISSION FOR ACCEPTANCE

FC 13
Submission for acceptance

FC 20
Providing the Service

CONTRACTOR PROVIDES THE SERVICE

Finish

Flow chart 23
Design of Equipment

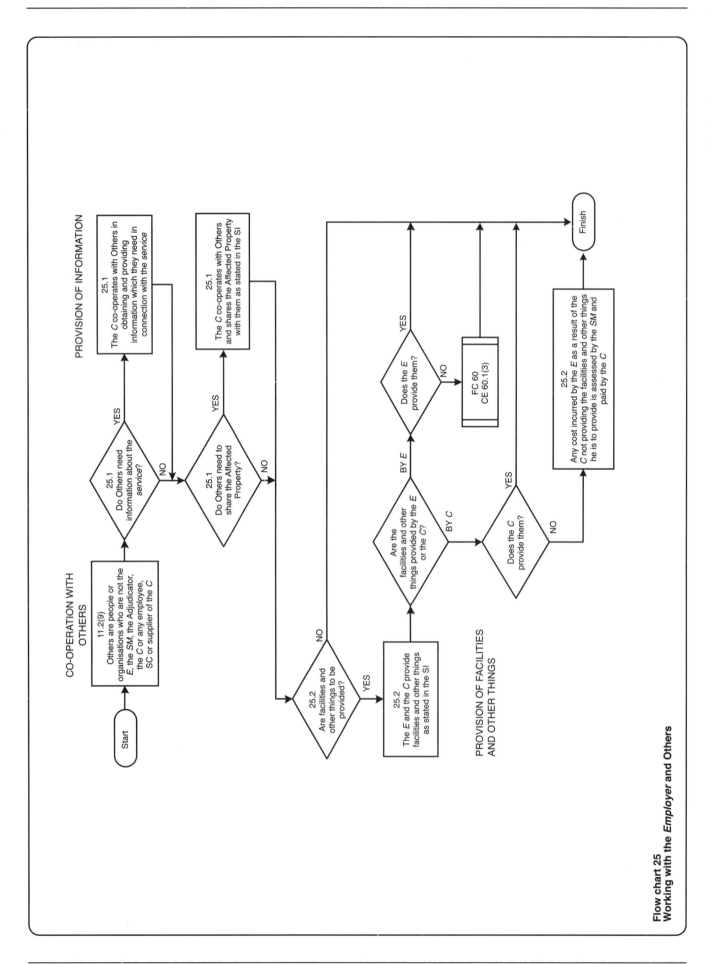

CO-OPERATION WITH OTHERS

PROVISION OF INFORMATION

Start

11.2(9)
Others are people or organisations who are not the *E*, the *SM*, the Adjudicator, the *C* or any employee, SC or supplier of the *C*

25.1
Do Others need information about the *service*?

YES →

25.1
The *C* co-operates with Others in obtaining and providing information which they need in connection with the *service*

NO

25.1
Do Others need to share the Affected Property?

YES →

25.1
The *C* co-operates with Others and shares the Affected Property with them as stated in the SI

NO

25.2
Are facilities and other things to be provided?

NO

YES →

25.2
The *E* and the *C* provide facilities and other things as stated in the SI

Are the facilities and other things provided by the *E* or the *C*?

BY *E* →

Does the *E* provide them?

YES →

NO

FC 60
CE 60.1(3)

BY *C*

Does the *C* provide them?

YES

NO →

25.2
Any cost incurred by the *E* as a result of the *C* not providing the facilities and other things he is to provide is assessed by the *SM* and paid by the *C*

→ **Finish**

PROVISION OF FACILITIES AND OTHER THINGS

Flow chart 25
Working with the *Employer* and Others

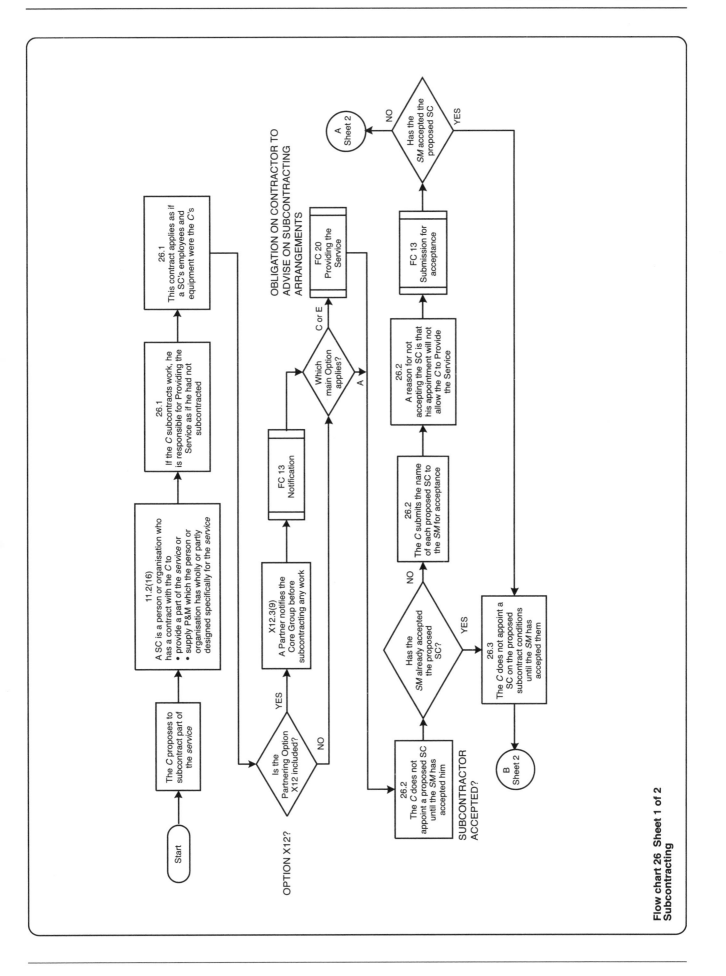

Flow chart 26 Sheet 1 of 2
Subcontracting

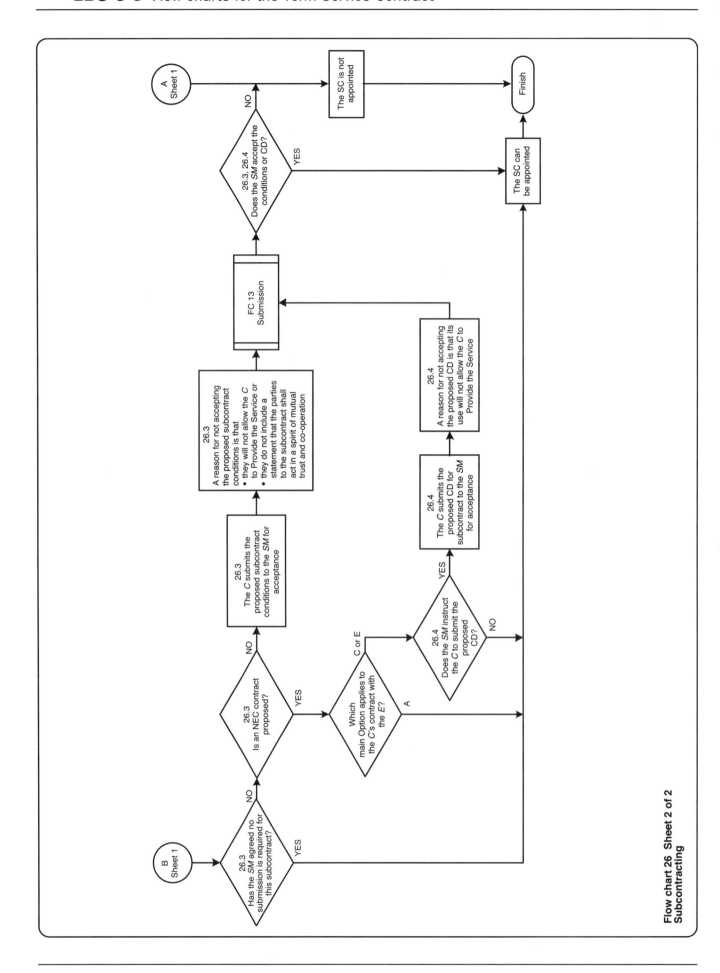

Flow chart 26 Sheet 2 of 2
Subcontracting

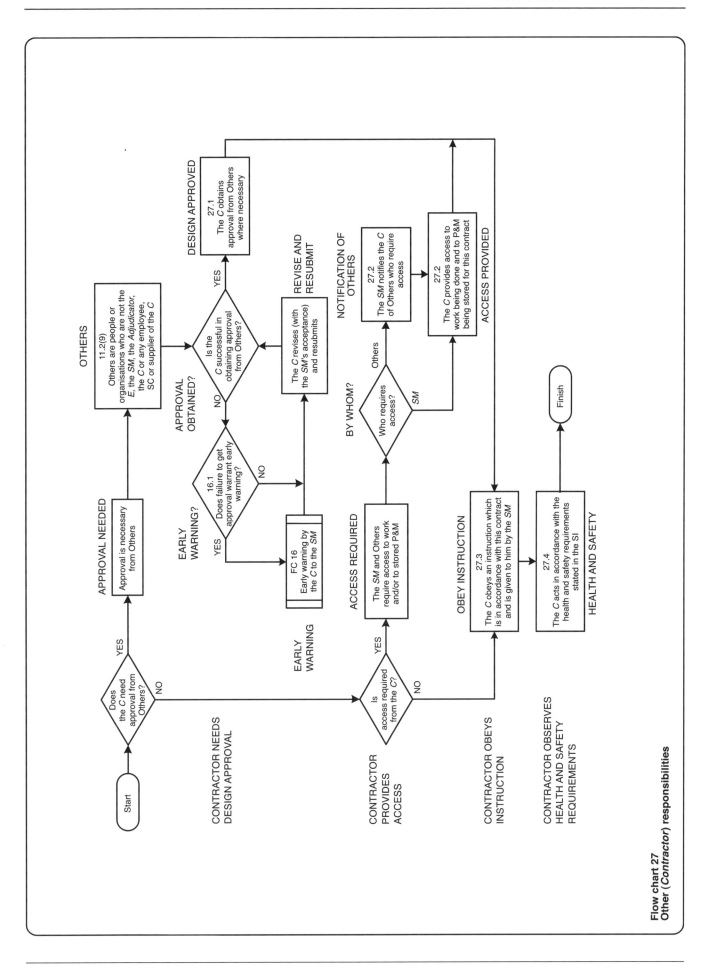

Flow chart 27
Other (*Contractor*) responsibilities

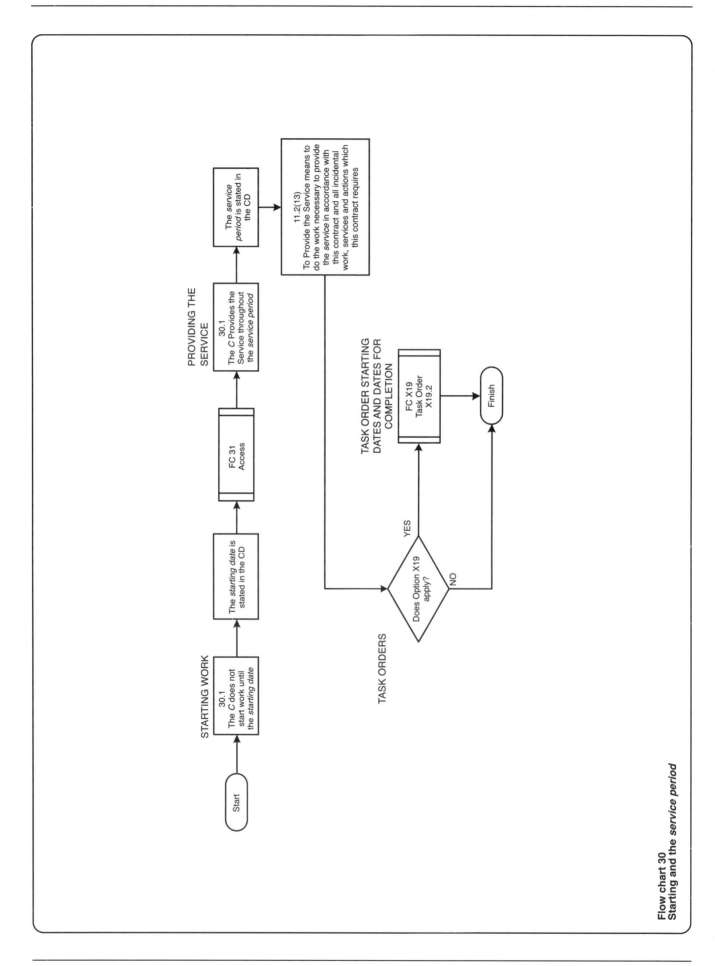

STARTING WORK

Start

30.1
The C does not start work until the *starting date*

The *starting date* is stated in the CD

FC 31
Access

PROVIDING THE SERVICE

30.1
The C Provides the Service throughout the *service period*

The *service period* is stated in the CD

11.2(13)
To Provide the Service means to do the work necessary to provide the *service* in accordance with this contract and all incidental work, services and actions which this contract requires

TASK ORDERS

Does Option X19 apply?

YES

NO

TASK ORDER STARTING DATES AND DATES FOR COMPLETION

FC X19
Task Order X19.2

Finish

Flow chart 30
Starting and the *service period*

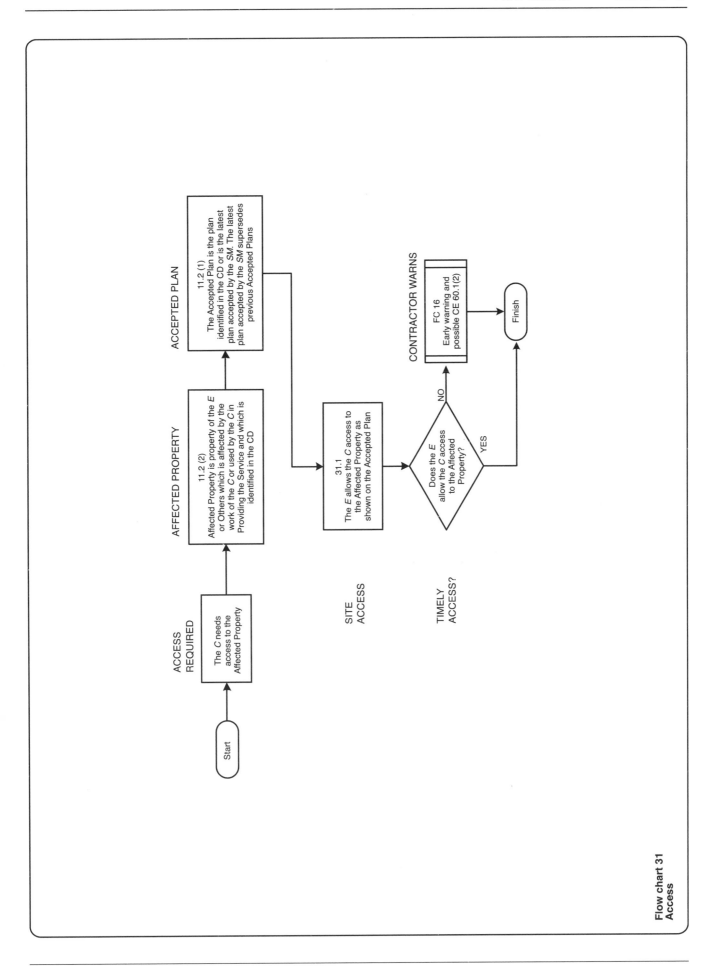

ACCESS
REQUIRED

The *C* needs
access to the
Affected Property

AFFECTED PROPERTY

11.2 (2)
Affected Property is property of the *E*
or Others which is affected by the
work of the *C* or used by the *C* in
Providing the Service and which is
identified in the CD

ACCEPTED PLAN

11.2 (1)
The Accepted Plan is the plan
identified in the CD or is the latest
plan accepted by the *SM*. The latest
plan accepted by the *SM* supersedes
previous Accepted Plans

Start

SITE
ACCESS

31.1
The *E* allows the *C* access to
the Affected Property as
shown on the Accepted Plan

TIMELY
ACCESS?

Does the *E*
allow the *C* access
to the Affected
Property?

NO

YES

CONTRACTOR WARNS

FC 16
Early warning and
possible CE 60.1(2)

Finish

**Flow chart 31
Access**

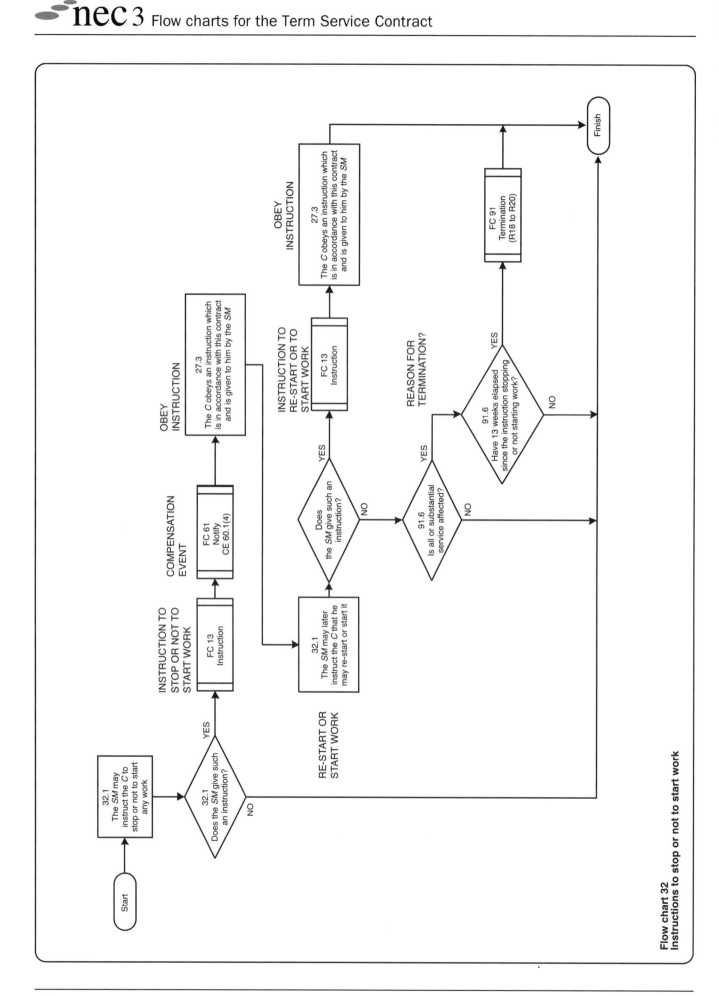
Start

32.1
The *SM* may instruct the *C* to stop or not to start any work

32.1
Does the *SM* give such an instruction?

INSTRUCTION TO STOP OR NOT TO START WORK

FC 13
Instruction

COMPENSATION EVENT

FC 61
Notify
CE 60.1(4)

OBEY INSTRUCTION

27.3
The *C* obeys an instruction which is in accordance with this contract and is given to him by the *SM*

YES

NO

RE-START OR START WORK

32.1
The *SM* may later instruct the *C* that he may re-start or start it

Does the *SM* give such an instruction?

YES

NO

INSTRUCTION TO RE-START OR TO START WORK

FC 13
Instruction

OBEY INSTRUCTION

27.3
The *C* obeys an instruction which is in accordance with this contract and is given to him by the *SM*

REASON FOR TERMINATION?

91.6
Is all or substantial service affected?

YES

NO

91.6
Have 13 weeks elapsed since the instruction stopping or not starting work?

YES

NO

FC 91
Termination
(R18 to R20)

Finish

Flow chart 32
Instructions to stop or not to start work

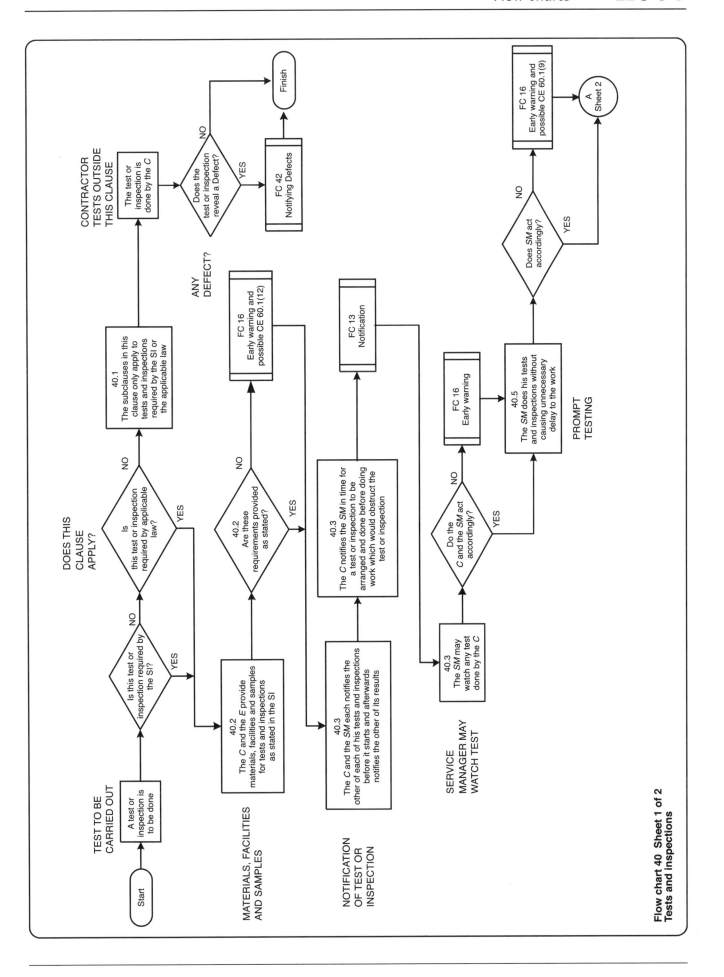

Flow chart 40 Sheet 1 of 2
Tests and inspections

23

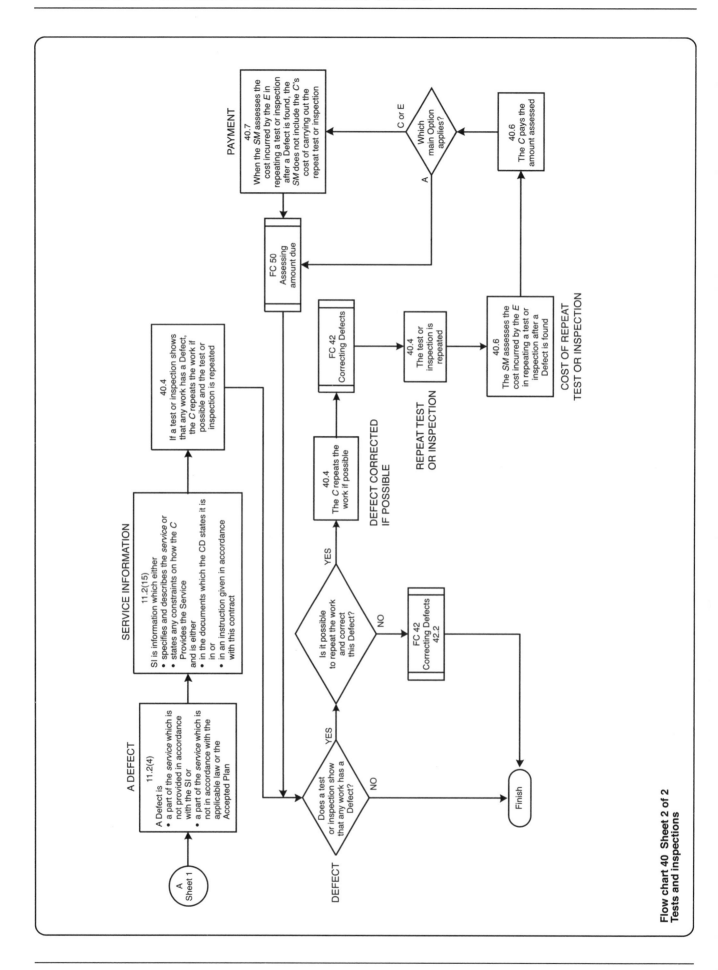

PAYMENT

40.7
When the *SM* assesses the cost incurred by the *E* in repeating a test or inspection after a Defect is found, the *SM* does not include the *C*'s cost of carrying out the repeat test or inspection

Which main Option applies?

C or E

A

40.6
The *C* pays the amount assessed

FC 50
Assessing amount due

SERVICE INFORMATION

11.2(15)

SI is information which either
• specifies and describes the *service* or
• states any constraints on how the *C* Provides the Service
and is either
• in the documents which the CD states it is in or
• in an instruction given in accordance with this contract

40.4
If a test or inspection shows that any work has a Defect, the *C* repeats the work if possible and the test or inspection is repeated

FC 42
Correcting Defects

40.4
The test or inspection is repeated

40.6
The *SM* assesses the cost incurred by the *E* in repeating a test or inspection after a Defect is found

COST OF REPEAT
TEST OR INSPECTION

REPEAT TEST
OR INSPECTION

40.4
The *C* repeats the work if possible

DEFECT CORRECTED
IF POSSIBLE

A DEFECT

11.2(4)

A Defect is
• a part of the *service* which is not provided in accordance with the SI or
• a part of the *service* which is not in accordance with the applicable law or the Accepted Plan

Is it possible to repeat the work and correct this Defect?

YES

NO

FC 42
Correcting Defects 42.2

A
Sheet 1

YES

Does a test or inspection show that any work has a Defect?

NO

DEFECT

Finish

Flow chart **40 Sheet 2 of 2**
Tests and inspections

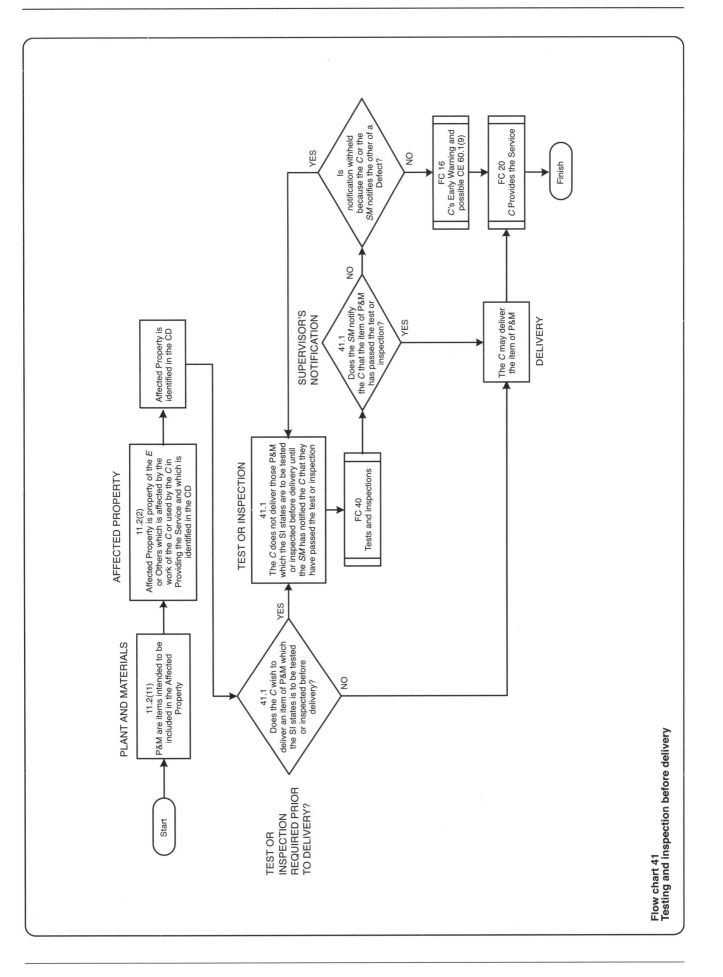

PLANT AND MATERIALS

11.2(11)
P&M are items intended to be included in the Affected Property

AFFECTED PROPERTY

11.2(2)
Affected Property is property of the *E* or Others which is affected by the work of the *C* or used by the *C* in Providing the Service and which is identified in the CD

Affected Property is identified in the CD

TEST OR INSPECTION

41.1
The *C* does not deliver those P&M which the SI states are to be tested or inspected before delivery until the *SM* has notified the *C* that they have passed the test or inspection

FC 40
Tests and inspections

TEST OR INSPECTION REQUIRED PRIOR TO DELIVERY?

41.1
Does the *C* wish to deliver an item of P&M which the SI states is to be tested or inspected before delivery?

YES

NO

SUPERVISOR'S NOTIFICATION

41.1
Does the *SM* notify the *C* that the item of P&M has passed the test or inspection?

YES

NO

Is notification withheld because the *C* or the *SM* notifies the other of a Defect?

YES

NO

FC 16
C's Early Warning and possible CE 60.1(9)

FC 20
C Provides the Service

DELIVERY

The *C* may deliver the item of P&M

Start

Finish

**Flow chart 41
Testing and inspection before delivery**

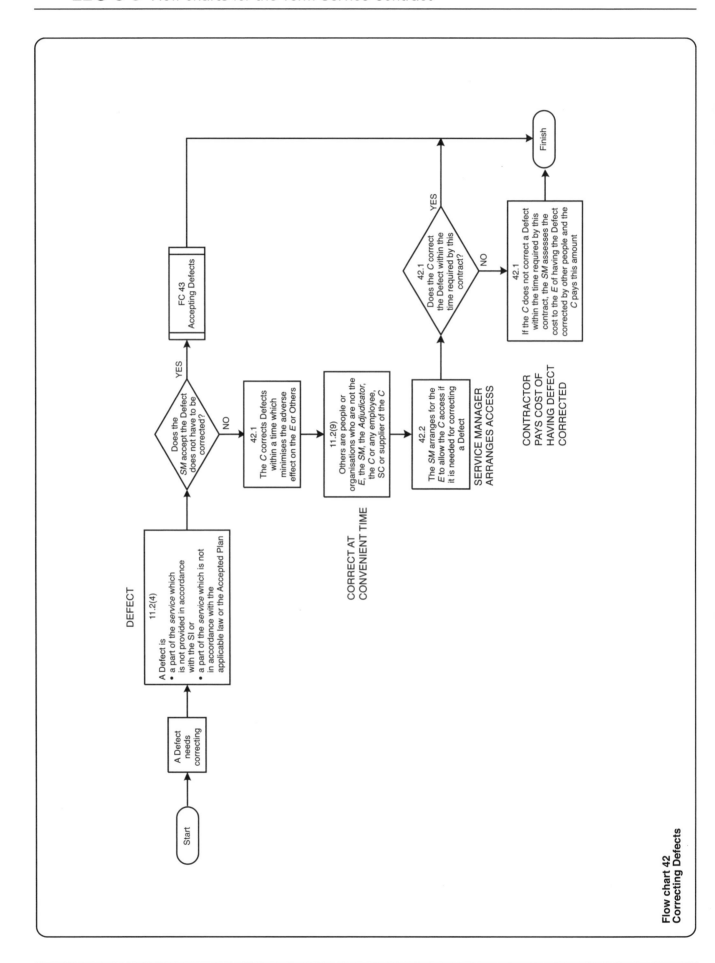

Start

A Defect needs correcting

DEFECT

11.2(4)

A Defect is
• a part of the *service* which is not provided in accordance with the SI or
• a part of the *service* which is not in accordance with the applicable law or the Accepted Plan

Does the *SM* accept the Defect does not have to be corrected?

YES → FC 43 Accepting Defects

NO

42.1

The *C* corrects Defects within a time which minimises the adverse effect on the *E* or Others

11.2(9)

Others are people or organisations who are not the *E*, the *SM*, the *Adjudicator*, the *C* or any employee, SC or supplier of the *C*

CORRECT AT CONVENIENT TIME

42.2

The *SM* arranges for the *E* to allow the *C* access if it is needed for correcting a Defect

SERVICE MANAGER ARRANGES ACCESS

42.1

Does the *C* correct the Defect within the time required by this contract?

YES → Finish

NO

42.1

If the *C* does not correct a Defect within the time required by this contract, the *SM* assesses the cost to the *E* of having the Defect corrected by other people and the *C* pays this amount

CONTRACTOR PAYS COST OF HAVING DEFECT CORRECTED

Flow chart 42
Correcting Defects

     www.neccontract.com

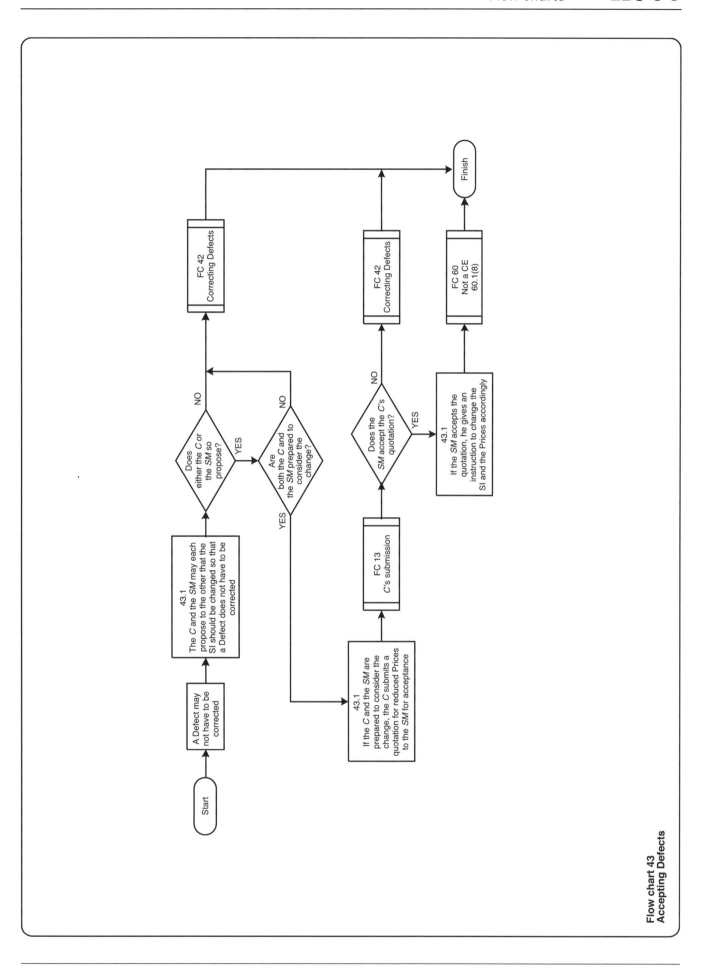

Start

A Defect may not have to be corrected

43.1
The C and the SM may each propose to the other that the SI should be changed so that a Defect does not have to be corrected

Does either the C or the SM so propose?

NO → FC 42
Correcting Defects → Finish

YES

Are both the C and the SM prepared to consider the change?

NO → FC 42
Correcting Defects

YES

43.1
If the C and the SM are prepared to consider the change, the C submits a quotation for reduced Prices to the SM for acceptance

FC 13
C's submission

Does the SM accept the C's quotation?

NO → FC 42
Correcting Defects → Finish

YES

43.1
If the SM accepts the quotation, he gives an instruction to change the SI and the Prices accordingly

FC 60
Not a CE
60.1(8) → Finish

Flow chart 43
Accepting Defects

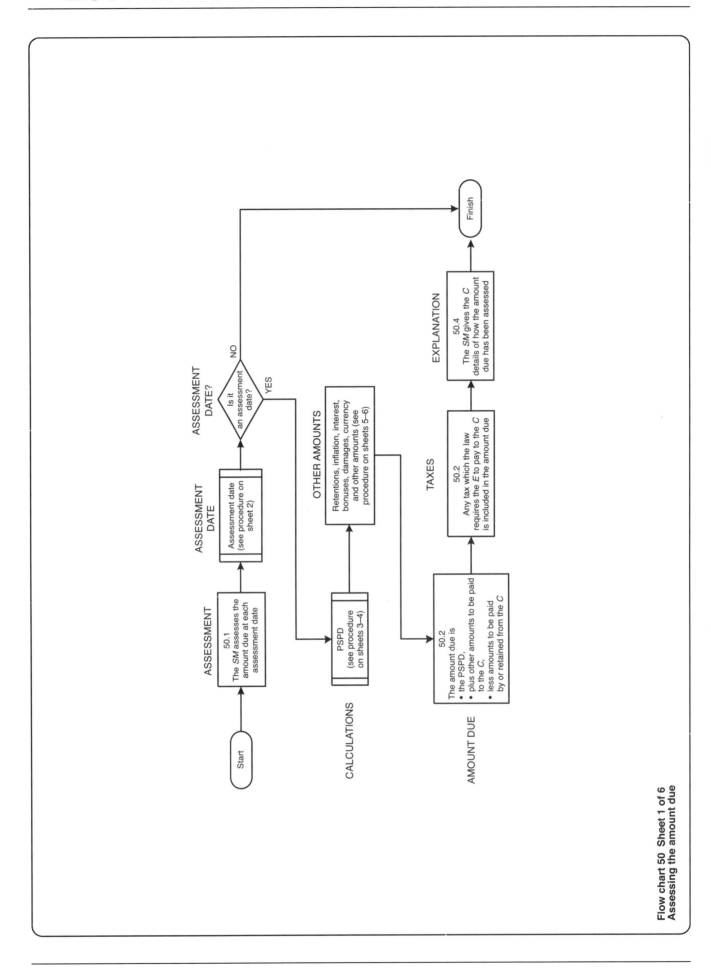

ASSESSMENT

50.1
The *SM* assesses the amount due at each assessment date

ASSESSMENT DATE

Assessment date (see procedure on sheet 2)

ASSESSMENT DATE?

Is it an assessment date?

NO

YES

Start

CALCULATIONS

PSPD
(see procedure on sheets 3–4)

OTHER AMOUNTS

Retentions, inflation, interest, bonuses, damages, currency and other amounts (see procedure on sheets 5–6)

TAXES

50.2
Any tax which the law requires the *E* to pay to the *C* is included in the amount due

EXPLANATION

50.4
The *SM* gives the *C* details of how the amount due has been assessed

Finish

AMOUNT DUE

50.2
The amount due is
• the PSPD,
• plus other amounts to be paid to the *C*,
• less amounts to be paid by or retained from the *C*

Flow chart 50 Sheet 1 of 6
Assessing the amount due

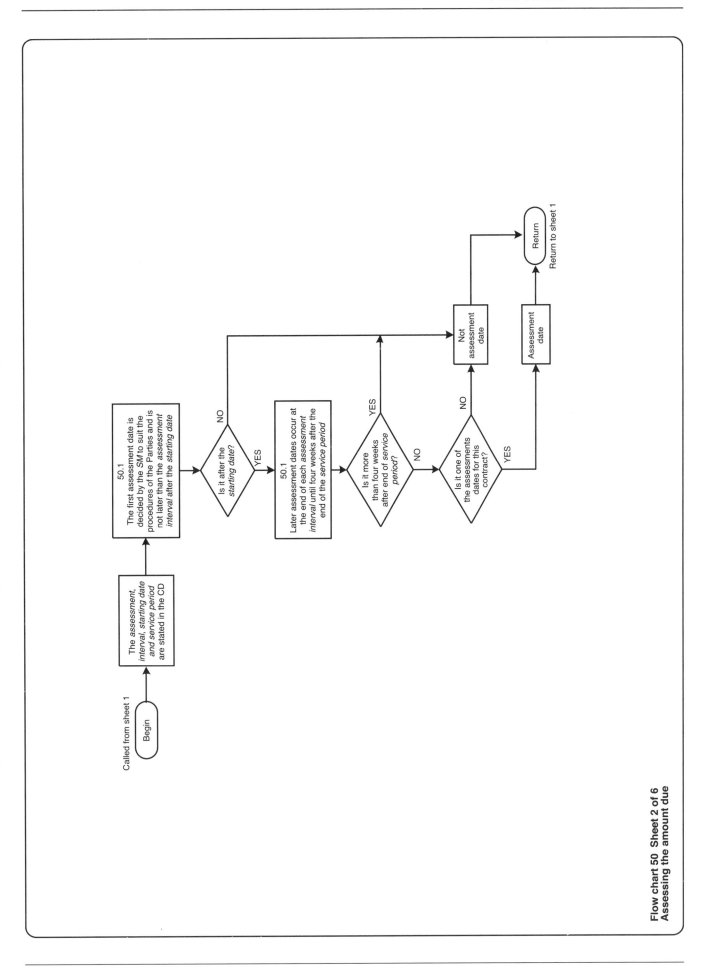

Flow chart 50 Sheet 2 of 6
Assessing the amount due

© copyright nec 2005

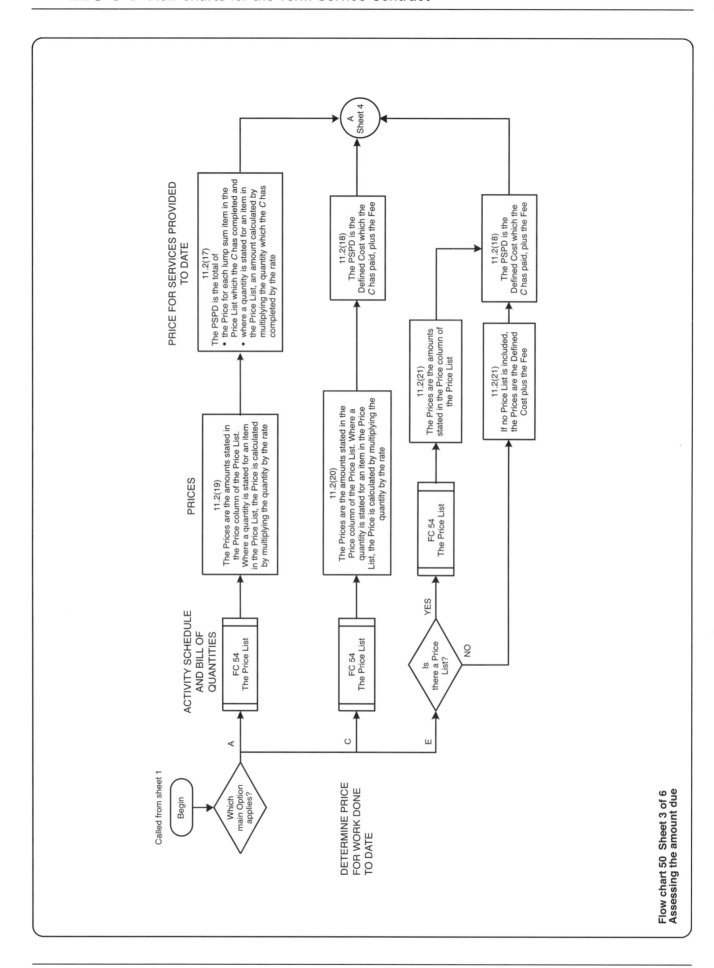

PRICE FOR SERVICES PROVIDED TO DATE

11.2(17)
The PSPD is the total of
- the Price for each lump sum item in the Price List which the *C* has completed and
- where a quantity is stated for an item in the Price List, an amount calculated by multiplying the quantity which the *C* has completed by the rate

PRICES

11.2(19)
The Prices are the amounts stated in the Price column of the Price List. Where a quantity is stated for an item in the Price List, the Price is calculated by multiplying the quantity by the rate

ACTIVITY SCHEDULE AND BILL OF QUANTITIES

FC 54
The Price List

Called from sheet 1

Begin

Which main Option applies?

A

DETERMINE PRICE FOR WORK DONE TO DATE

C

FC 54
The Price List

11.2(20)
The Prices are the amounts stated in the Price column of the Price List. Where a quantity is stated for an item in the Price List, Price is calculated by multiplying the quantity by rate

11.2(18)
The PSPD is the Defined Cost which the *C* has paid, plus the Fee

E

Is there a Price List?

YES

FC 54
The Price List

11.2(21)
The Prices are the amounts stated in the Price column of the Price List

NO

11.2(21)
If no Price List is included, the Prices are the Defined Cost plus the Fee

11.2(18)
The PSPD is the Defined Cost which the *C* has paid, plus the Fee

A
Sheet 4

Flow chart 50 Sheet 3 of 6
Assessing the amount due

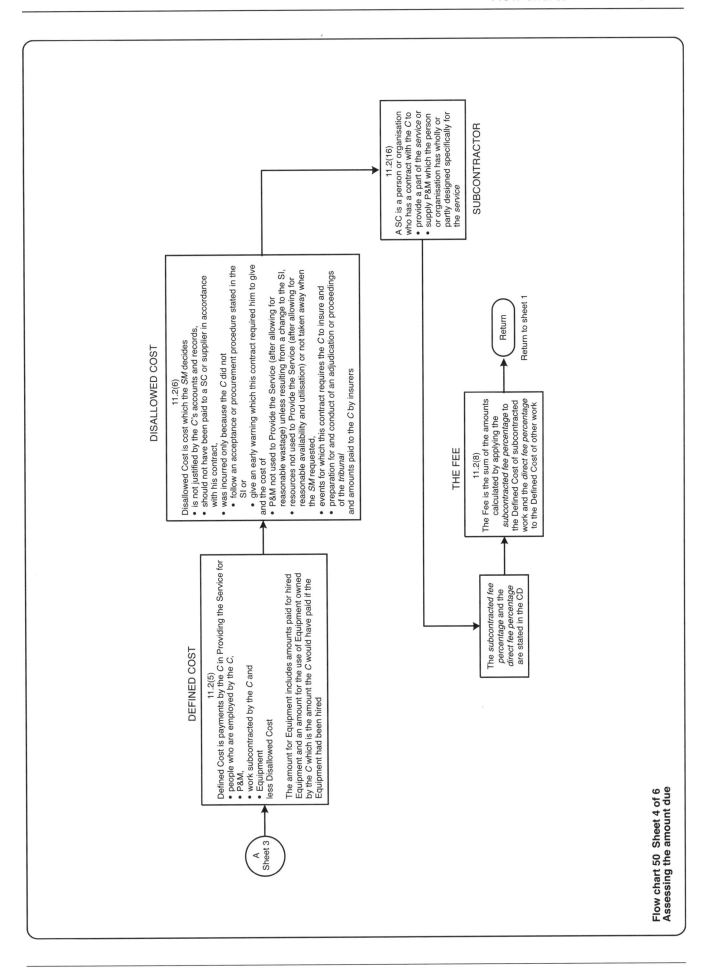

DEFINED COST

11.2(5)

Defined Cost is payments by the *C* in Providing the Service for
- people who are employed by the *C*,
- P&M,
- work subcontracted by the *C* and
- Equipment

less Disallowed Cost

The amount for Equipment includes amounts paid for hired Equipment and an amount for the use of Equipment owned by the *C* which is the amount the *C* would have paid if the Equipment had been hired

A
Sheet 3

DISALLOWED COST

11.2(6)

Disallowed Cost is cost which the *SM* decides
- is not justified by the *C's* accounts and records,
- should not have been paid to a SC or supplier in accordance with his contract,
- was incurred only because the *C* did not
  - follow an acceptance or procurement procedure stated in the SI or
  - give an early warning which this contract required him to give

and the cost of
- P&M not used to Provide the Service (after allowing for reasonable wastage) unless resulting from a change to the SI,
- resources not used to Provide the Service (after allowing for reasonable availability and utilisation) or not taken away when the *SM* requested,
- events for which this contract requires the *C* to insure and
- preparation for and conduct of an adjudication or proceedings of the *tribunal*

and amounts paid to the *C* by insurers

SUBCONTRACTOR

11.2(16)

A SC is a person or organisation who has a contract with the *C* to
- provide a part of the *service* or
- supply P&M which the person or organisation has wholly or partly designed specifically for the *service*

THE FEE

11.2(8)

The Fee is the sum of the amounts calculated by applying the *subcontracted fee percentage* to the Defined Cost of subcontracted work and the *direct fee percentage* to the Defined Cost of other work

The *subcontracted fee percentage* and the *direct fee percentage* are stated in the CD

Return

Return to sheet 1

Flow chart 50 Sheet 4 of 6
Assessing the amount due

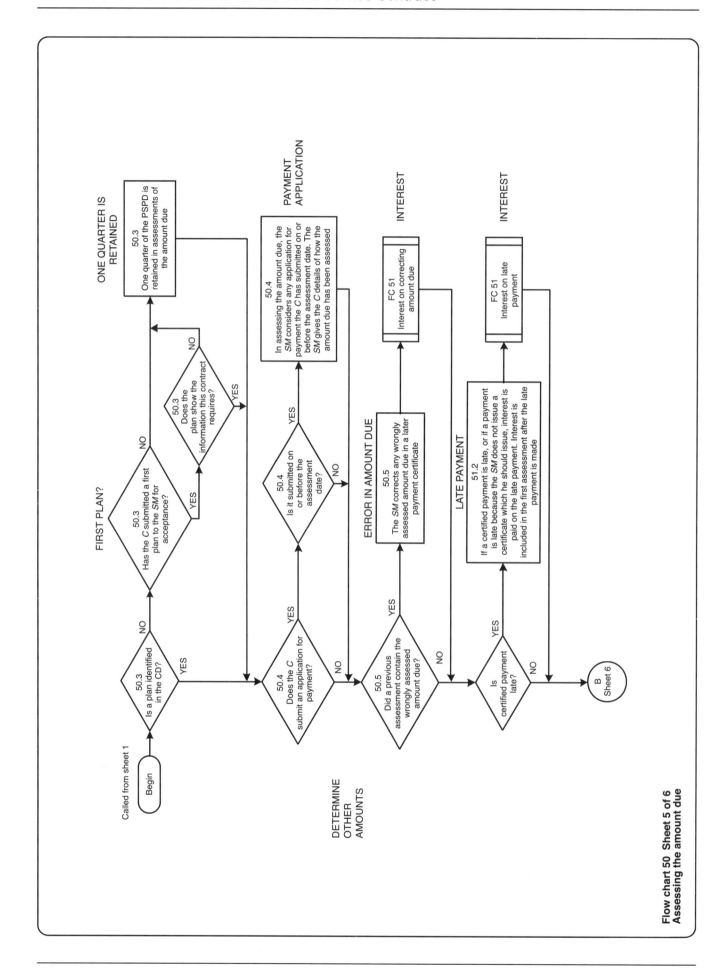

FIRST PLAN?

ONE QUARTER IS RETAINED

PAYMENT APPLICATION

INTEREST

INTEREST

DETERMINE OTHER AMOUNTS

ERROR IN AMOUNT DUE

LATE PAYMENT

Called from sheet 1

Begin

50.3
Is a plan identified in the CD?

50.3
Has the C submitted a first plan to the SM for acceptance?

50.3
Does the plan show the information this contract requires?

50.3
One quarter of the PSPD is retained in assessments of the amount due

50.4
Does the C submit an application for payment?

50.4
Is it submitted on or before the assessment date?

50.4
In assessing the amount due, the SM considers any application for payment the C has submitted on or before the assessment date. The SM gives the C details of how the amount due has been assessed

50.5
Did a previous assessment contain the wrongly assessed amount due?

50.5
The SM corrects any wrongly assessed amount due in a later payment certificate

FC 51
Interest on correcting amount due

51.2
If a certified payment is late, or if a payment is late because the SM does not issue a certificate which he should issue, interest is paid on the late payment. Interest is included in the first assessment after the late payment is made

Is certified payment late?

FC 51
Interest on late payment

B
Sheet 6

**Flow chart 50 Sheet 5 of 6
Assessing the amount due**

www.neccontract.com

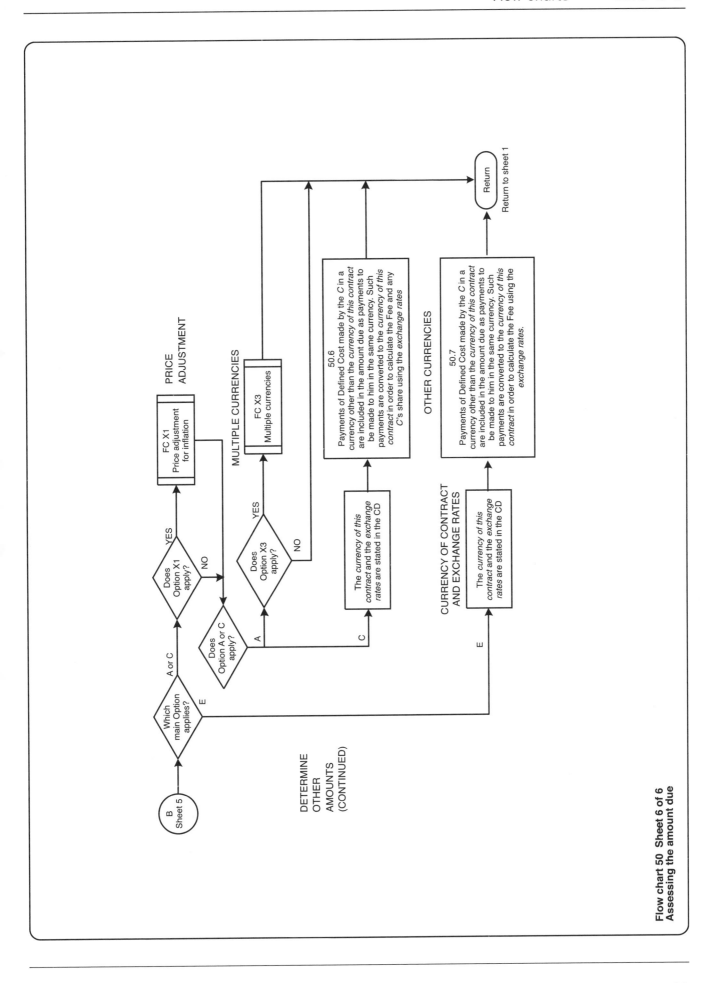
DETERMINE
OTHER
AMOUNTS
(CONTINUED)

B
Sheet 5

Which
main Option
applies?

A or C

E

Does
Option A or C
apply?

A

C

Does
Option X1
apply?

YES

NO

FC X1

Price adjustment
for inflation

PRICE
ADJUSTMENT

Does
Option X3
apply?

YES

NO

FC X3

Multiple currencies

MULTIPLE CURRENCIES

The *currency of this
contract* and the *exchange
rates* are stated in the CD

50.6

Payments of Defined Cost made by the *C* in a
currency other than the *currency of this contract*
are included in the amount due as payments to
be made to him in the same currency. Such
payments are converted to the *currency of this
contract* in order to calculate the Fee and any
C's share using the *exchange rates*

OTHER CURRENCIES

The *currency of this
contract* and the *exchange
rates* are stated in the CD

CURRENCY OF CONTRACT
AND EXCHANGE RATES

50.7

Payments of Defined Cost made by the *C* in a
currency other than the *currency of this contract*
are included in the amount due as payments to
be made to him in the same currency. Such
payments are converted to the *currency of this
contract* in order to calculate the Fee using the
exchange rates.

Return

Return to sheet 1

Flow chart 50 Sheet 6 of 6
Assessing the amount due

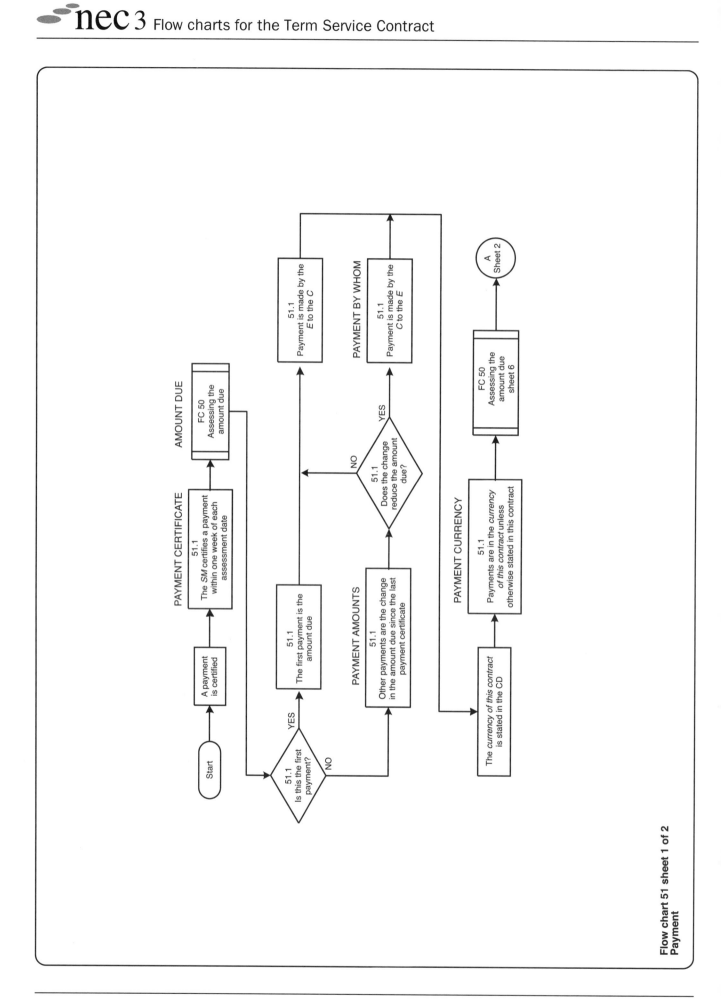

PAYMENT CERTIFICATE

AMOUNT DUE

Start

A payment is certified

51.1
The *SM* certifies a payment within one week of each assessment date

FC 50
Assessing the amount due

51.1
Is this the first payment?

YES

51.1
The first payment is the amount due

NO

51.1
Payment is made by the *E* to the *C*

PAYMENT AMOUNTS

51.1
Other payments are the change in the amount due since the last payment certificate

51.1
Does the change reduce the amount due?

NO

YES

PAYMENT BY WHOM

51.1
Payment is made by the *C* to the *E*

PAYMENT CURRENCY

The *currency of this contract* is stated in the CD

51.1
Payments are in the *currency of this contract* unless otherwise stated in this contract

FC 50
Assessing the amount due
sheet 6

A
Sheet 2

Flow chart 51 sheet 1 of 2
Payment

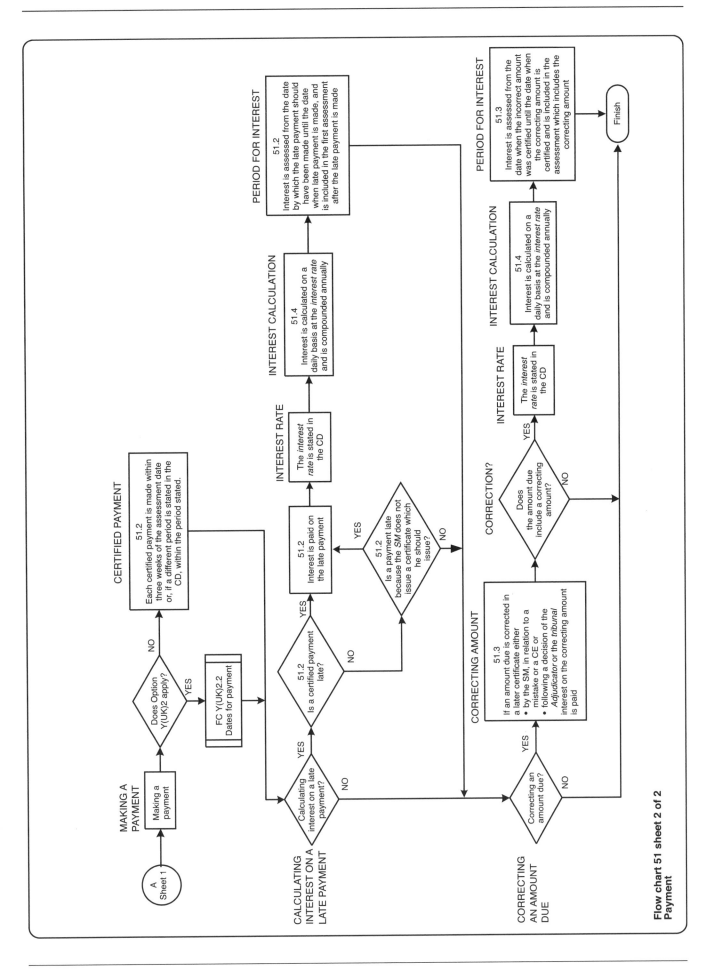

Flow chart 51 sheet 2 of 2
Payment

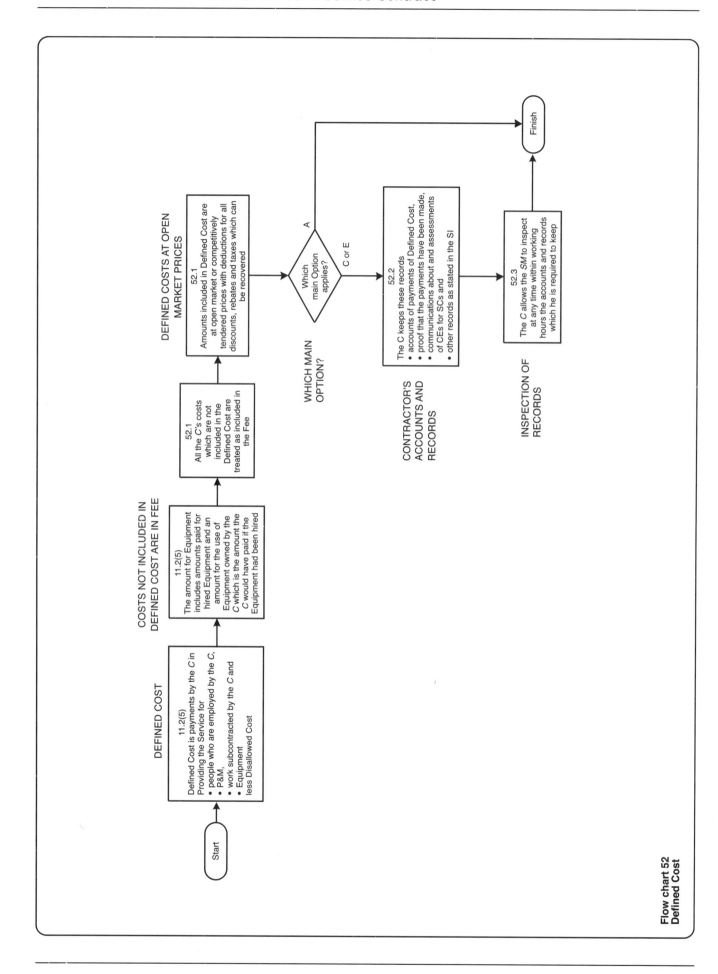

DEFINED COST

11.2(5)
Defined Cost is payments by the *C* in Providing the Service for
• people who are employed by the *C*,
• P&M,
• work subcontracted by the *C* and
• Equipment
less Disallowed Cost

COSTS NOT INCLUDED IN DEFINED COST ARE IN FEE

11.2(5)
The amount for Equipment includes amounts paid for hired Equipment and an amount for the use of Equipment owned by the *C* which is the amount the *C* would have paid if the Equipment had been hired

DEFINED COSTS AT OPEN MARKET PRICES

52.1
Amounts included in Defined Cost are at open market or competitively tendered prices with deductions for all discounts, rebates and taxes which can be recovered

52.1
All the *C*'s costs which are not included in the Defined Cost are treated as included in the Fee

WHICH MAIN OPTION?

Which main Option applies?

A

C or E

CONTRACTOR'S ACCOUNTS AND RECORDS

52.2
The C keeps these records
• accounts of payments of Defined Cost,
• proof that the payments have been made,
• communications about and assessments of CEs for SCs and
• other records as stated in the SI

INSPECTION OF RECORDS

52.3
The *C* allows the *SM* to inspect at any time within working hours the accounts and records which he is required to keep

Start

Finish

Flow chart 52
Defined Cost

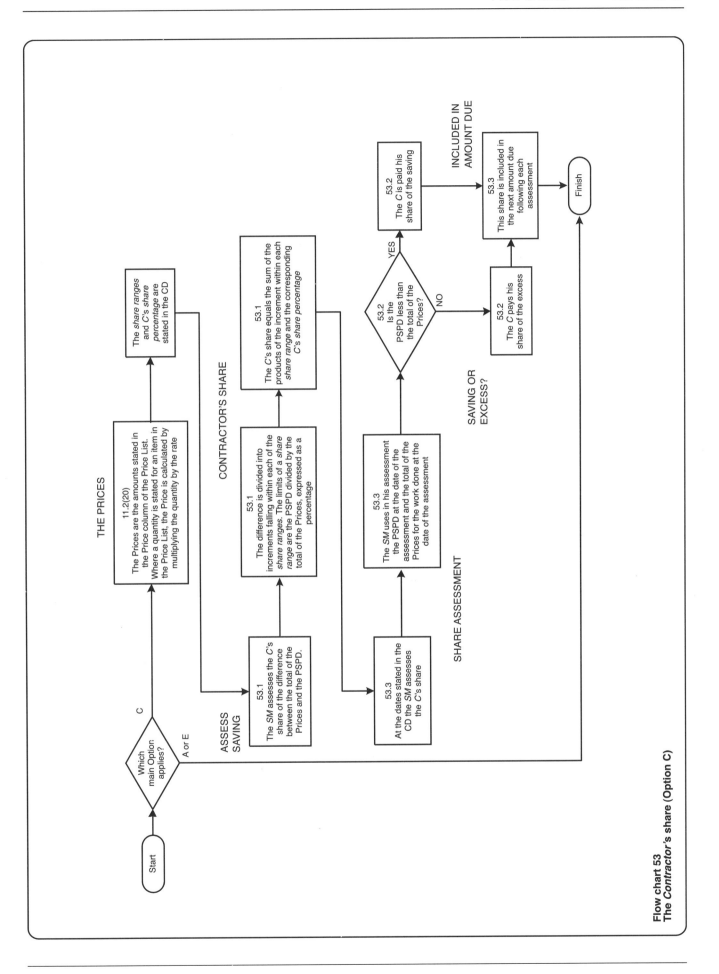

THE PRICES

11.2(20)
The Prices are the amounts stated in the Price column of the Price List. Where a quantity is stated for an item in the Price List, the Price is calculated by multiplying the quantity by the rate

The *share ranges* and *C's share percentage* are stated in the CD

CONTRACTOR'S SHARE

53.1
The *C's* share equals the sum of the products of the increment within each *share range* and the corresponding *C's share percentage*

53.1
The difference is divided into increments falling within each of the *share ranges*. The limits of a *share range* are the PSPD divided by the total of the Prices, expressed as a percentage

ASSESS SAVING

53.1
The *SM* assesses the *C's* share of the difference between the total of the Prices and the PSPD.

53.3
The *SM* uses in his assessment the PSPD at the date of the assessment and the total of the Prices for the work done at the date of the assessment

53.3
At the dates stated in the CD the *SM* assesses the *C's* share

SHARE ASSESSMENT

53.2
Is the PSPD less than the total of the Prices?

YES → **53.2** The *C* is paid his share of the saving

NO → **53.2** The *C* pays his share of the excess

SAVING OR EXCESS?

INCLUDED IN AMOUNT DUE

53.3
This share is included in the next amount due following each assessment

Start

Which main Option applies?

C

A or E

Finish

Flow chart 53
The *Contractor's* share (Option C)

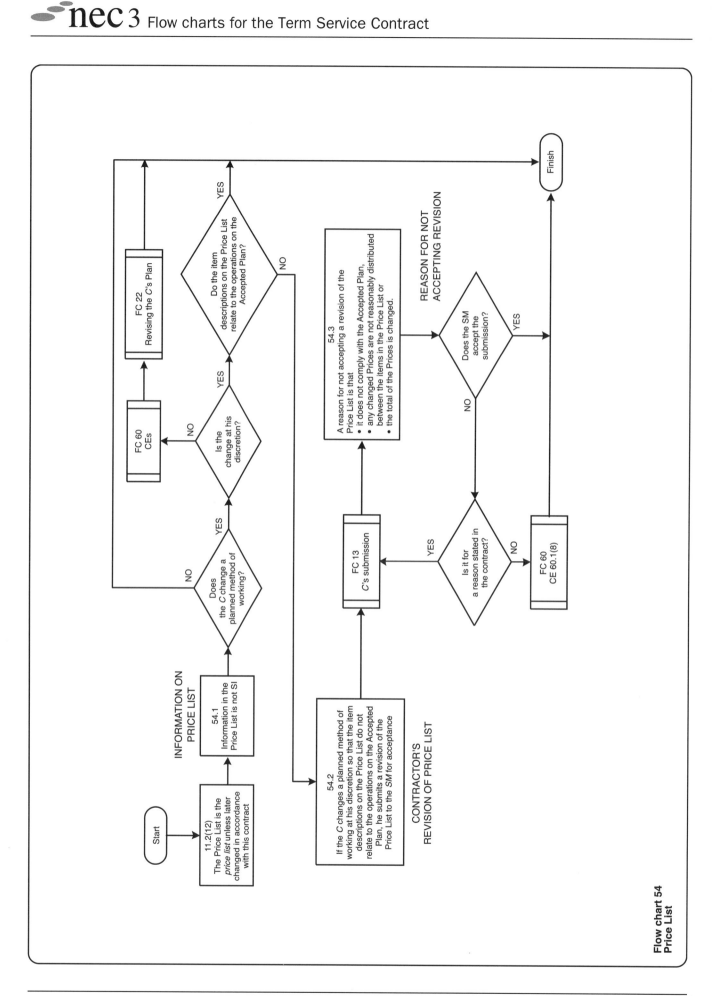

Flow chart 54
Price List

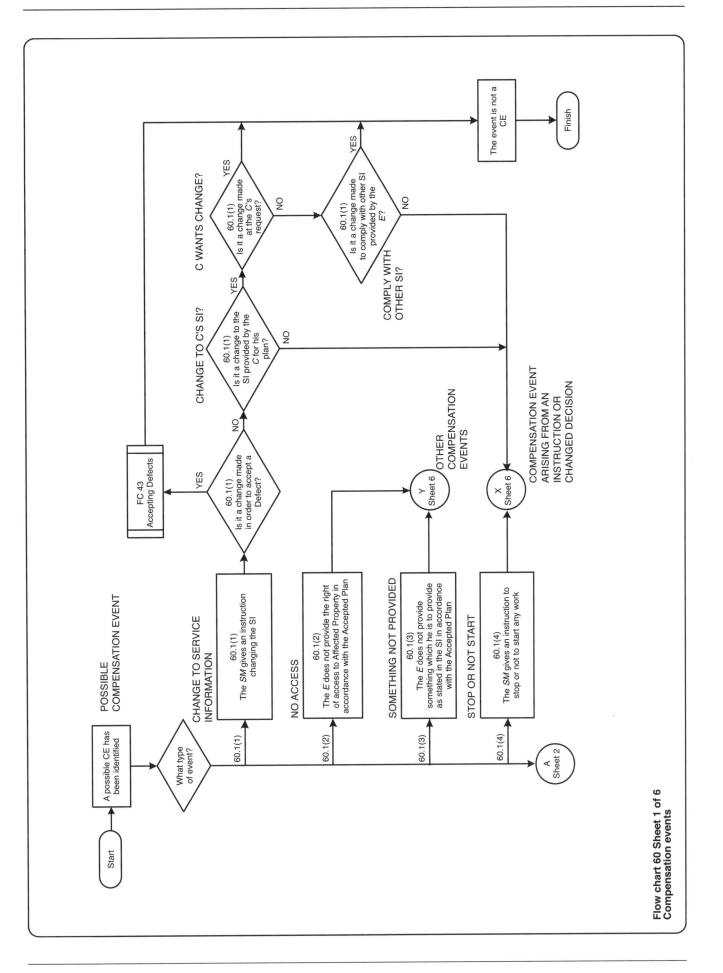

Flow chart 60 Sheet 1 of 6
Compensation events

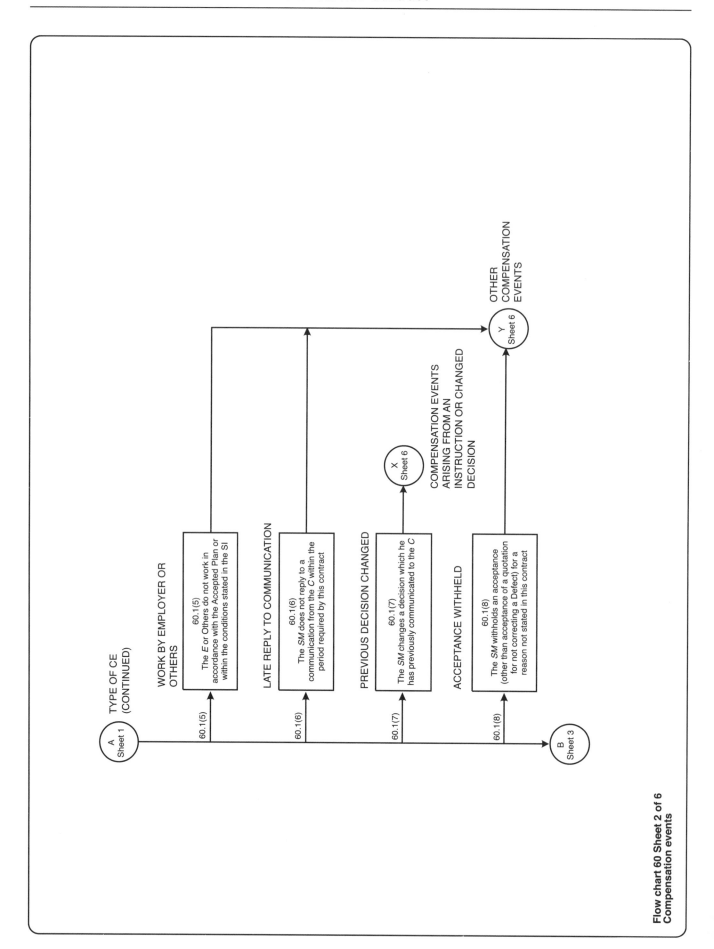

OTHER COMPENSATION EVENTS
Y Sheet 6

COMPENSATION EVENTS ARISING FROM AN INSTRUCTION OR CHANGED DECISION

X Sheet 6

TYPE OF CE (CONTINUED)

A Sheet 1

WORK BY EMPLOYER OR OTHERS

60.1(5)

60.1(5)
The *E* or Others do not work in accordance with the Accepted Plan or within the conditions stated in the SI

LATE REPLY TO COMMUNICATION

60.1(6)

60.1(6)
The *SM* does not reply to a communication from the *C* within the period required by this contract

PREVIOUS DECISION CHANGED

60.1(7)

60.1(7)
The *SM* changes a decision which he has previously communicated to the *C*

ACCEPTANCE WITHHELD

60.1(8)

60.1(8)
The *SM* withholds an acceptance (other than acceptance of a quotation for not correcting a Defect) for a reason not stated in this contract

B Sheet 3

Flow chart 60 Sheet 2 of 6
Compensation events

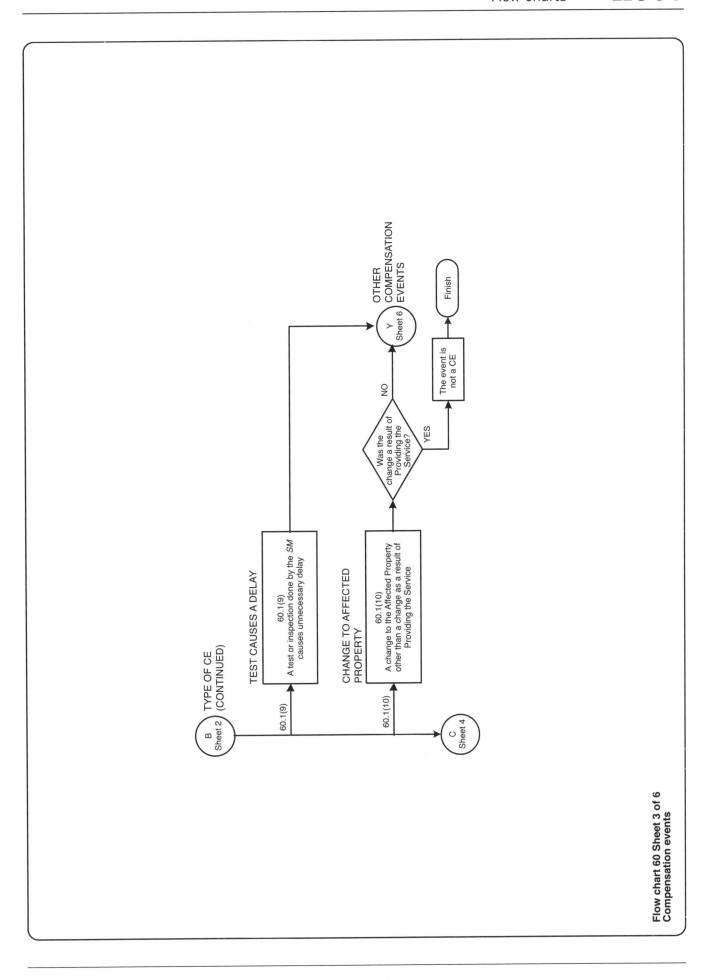

**Flow chart 60 Sheet 3 of 6
Compensation events**

© copyright nec 2005   41

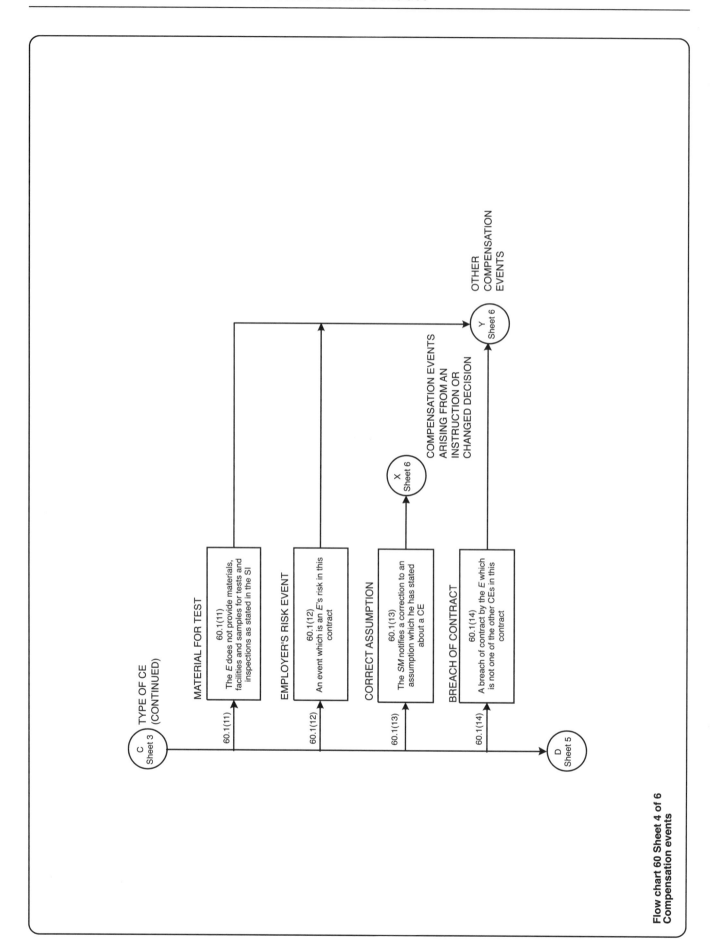

TYPE OF CE (CONTINUED)

C Sheet 3

MATERIAL FOR TEST

60.1(11)

The *E* does not provide materials, facilities and samples for tests and inspections as stated in the SI

60.1(11)

EMPLOYER'S RISK EVENT

60.1(12)

An event which is an *E*'s risk in this contract

60.1(12)

CORRECT ASSUMPTION

60.1(13)

The *SM* notifies a correction to an assumption which he has stated about a CE

60.1(13)

BREACH OF CONTRACT

60.1(14)

A breach of contract by the *E* which is not one of the other CEs in this contract

60.1(14)

X Sheet 6

COMPENSATION EVENTS ARISING FROM AN INSTRUCTION OR CHANGED DECISION

Y Sheet 6

OTHER COMPENSATION EVENTS

D Sheet 5

**Flow chart 60 Sheet 4 of 6
Compensation events**

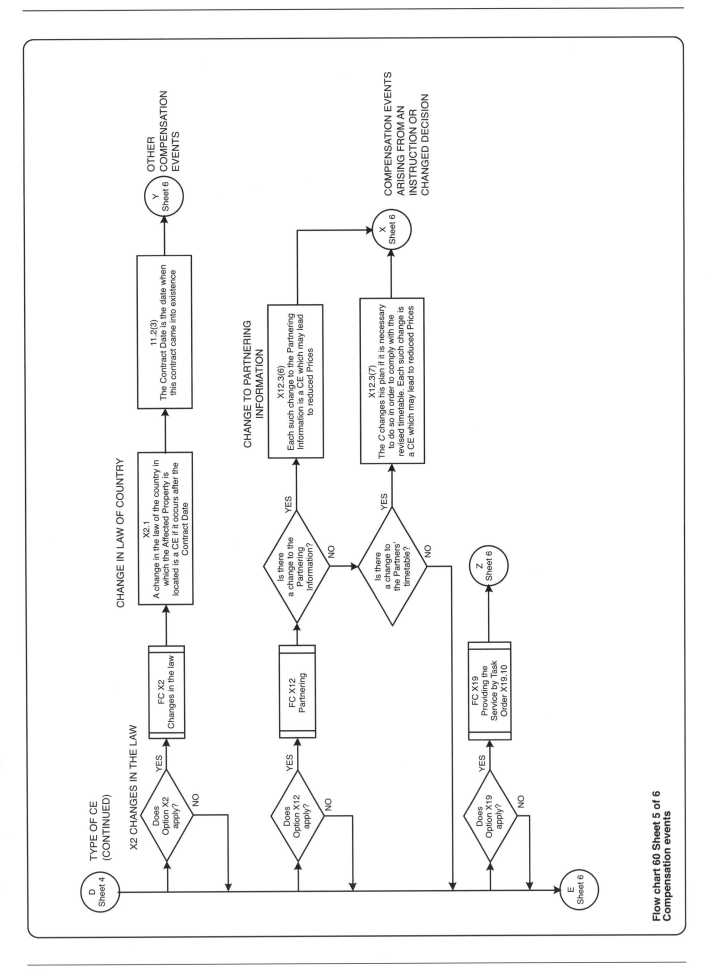

Flow chart 60 Sheet 5 of 6
Compensation events

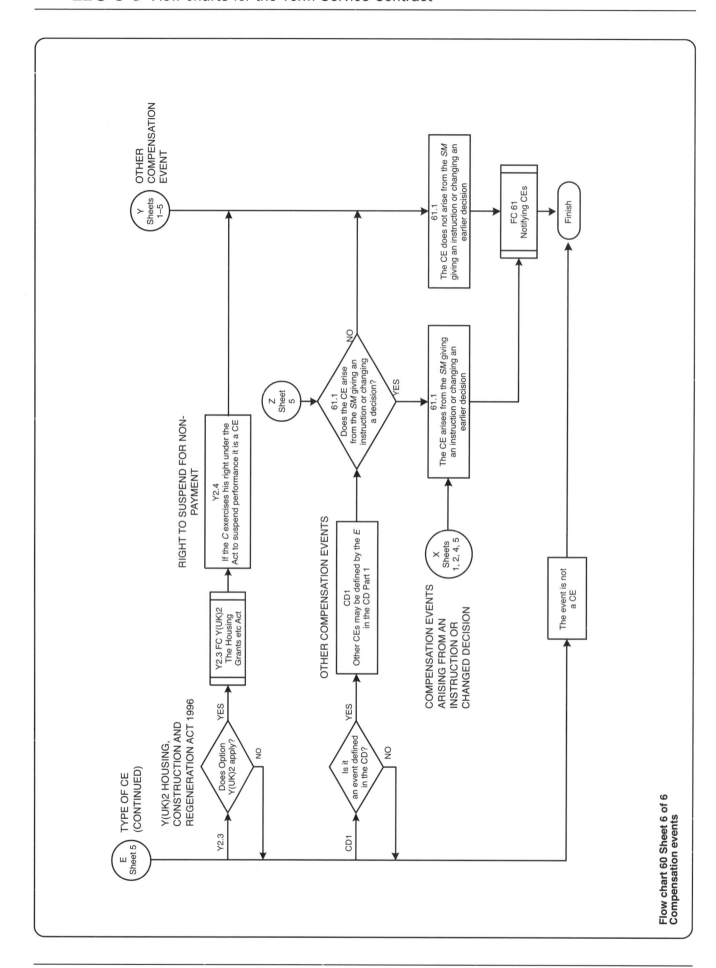

Flow chart 60 Sheet 6 of 6
Compensation events

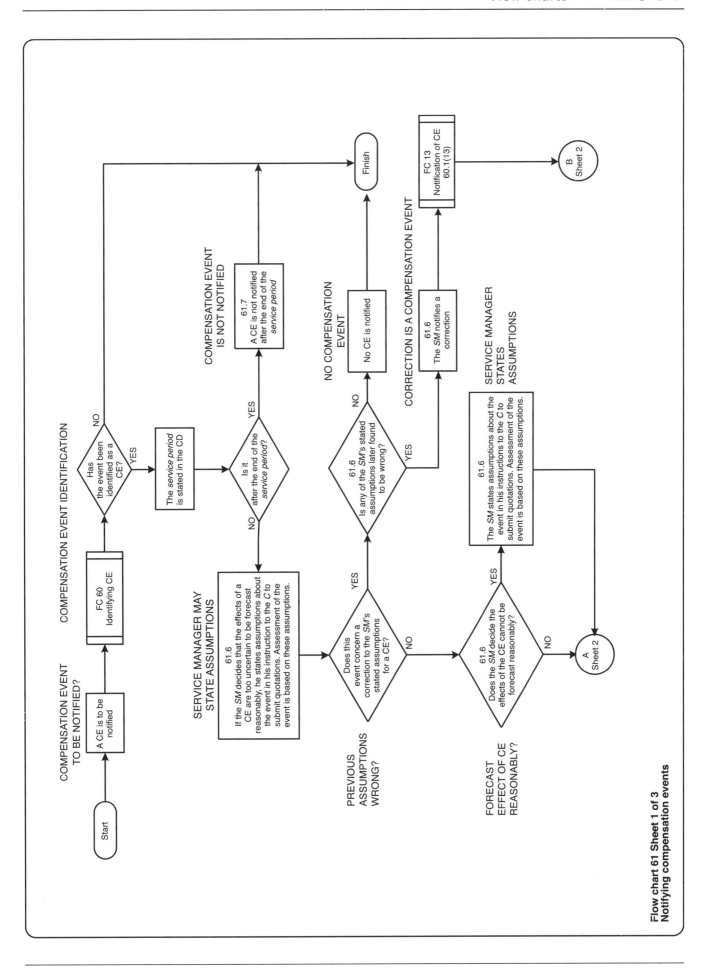

Flow chart 61 Sheet 1 of 3
Notifying compensation events

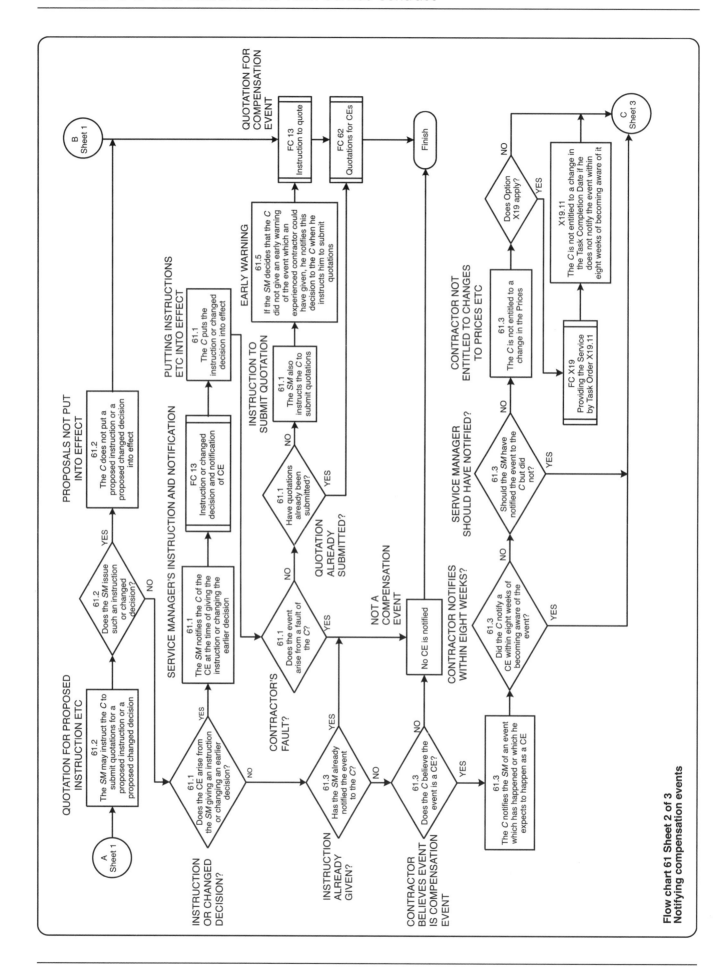

Flow chart 61 Sheet 2 of 3
Notifying compensation events

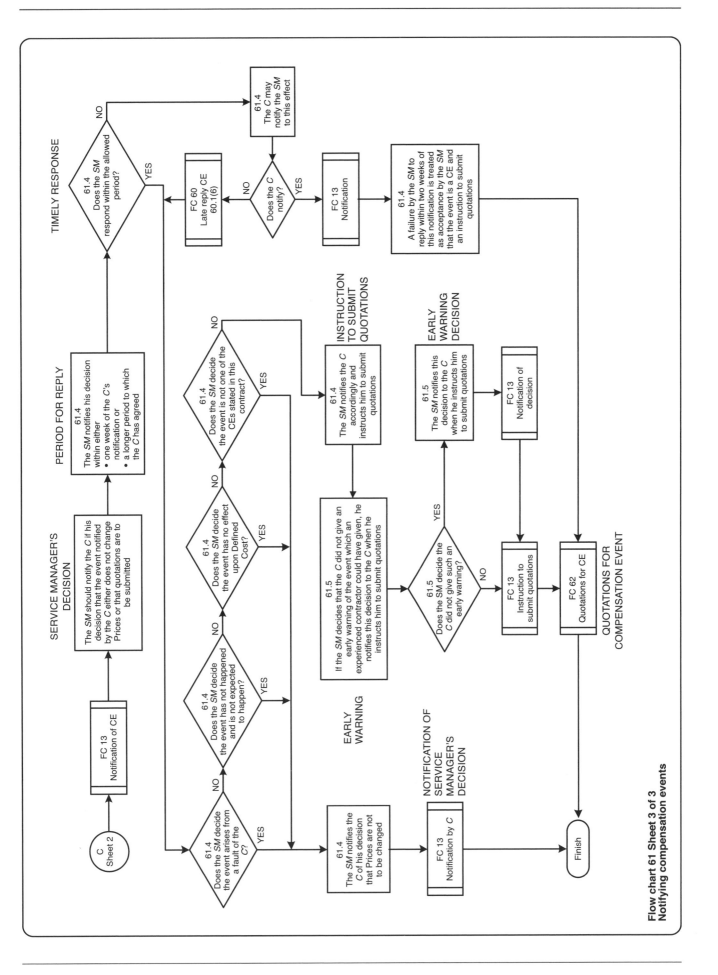

TIMELY RESPONSE

61.4
Does the *SM* respond within the allowed period?

61.4
The *C* may notify the *SM* to this effect

FC 60
Late reply CE 60.1(6)

61.4
Does the *C* notify?

FC 13
Notification

61.4
A failure by the *SM* to reply within two weeks of this notification is treated as acceptance by the *SM* that the event is a CE and an instruction to submit quotations

PERIOD FOR REPLY

61.4
The *SM* notifies his decision within either
• one week of the *C*'s notification or
• a longer period to which the *C* has agreed

SERVICE MANAGER'S DECISION

The *SM* should notify the *C* if his decision that the event notified by the *C* either does not change Prices or that quotations are to be submitted

61.4
Does the *SM* decide the event is not one of the CEs stated in this contract?

INSTRUCTION TO SUBMIT QUOTATIONS

61.4
The *SM* notifies the *C* accordingly and instructs him to submit quotations

EARLY WARNING DECISION

61.5
The *SM* notifies this decision to the *C* when he instructs him to submit quotations

FC 13
Notification of decision

61.4
Does the *SM* decide the event has no effect upon Defined Cost?

61.5
If the *SM* decides that the *C* did not give an early warning of the event which an experienced contractor could have given, he notifies this decision to the *C* when he instructs him to submit quotations

61.5
Does the *SM* decide the *C* did not give an early warning?

FC 13
Instruction to submit quotations

FC 62
Quotations for CE

QUOTATIONS FOR COMPENSATION EVENT

FC 13
Notification of CE

61.4
Does the *SM* decide the event has not happened and is not expected to happen?

EARLY WARNING

C
Sheet 2

61.4
Does the *SM* decide the event arises from a fault of the *C*?

NOTIFICATION OF SERVICE MANAGER'S DECISION

61.4
The *SM* notifies the *C* of his decision that Prices are not to be changed

FC 13
Notification by *C*

Finish

NO   YES

Flow chart 61 Sheet 3 of 3
Notifying compensation events

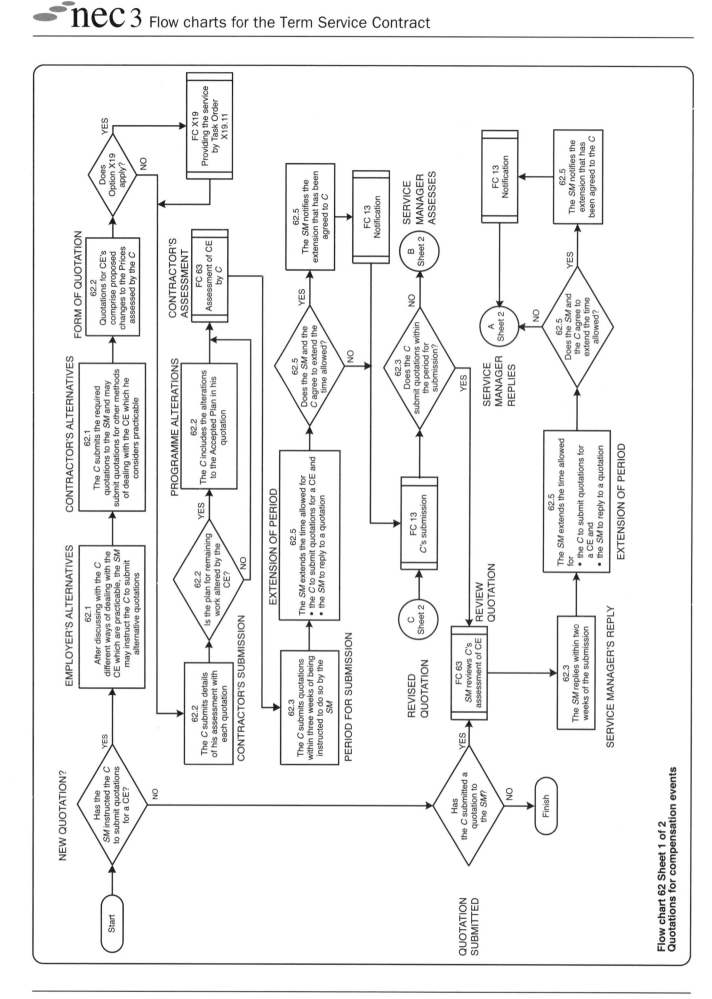

NEW QUOTATION?

Start

Has the *SM* instructed the *C* to submit quotations for a CE?

YES / NO

EMPLOYER'S ALTERNATIVES

62.1
After discussing with the *C* different ways of dealing with the CE which are practicable, the *SM* may instruct the *C* to submit alternative quotations

CONTRACTOR'S ALTERNATIVES

62.1
The *C* submits the required quotations to the *SM* and may submit quotations for other methods of dealing with the CE which he considers practicable

FORM OF QUOTATION

62.2
Quotations for CE's comprise proposed changes to the Prices assessed by the *C*

Does Option X19 apply?

YES / NO

FC X19
Providing the service by Task Order X19.11

CONTRACTOR'S SUBMISSION

62.2
The *C* submits details of his assessment with each quotation

62.2
Is the plan for remaining work altered by the CE?

YES / NO

PROGRAMME ALTERATIONS

62.2
The *C* includes the alterations to the Accepted Plan in his quotation

CONTRACTOR'S ASSESSMENT

FC 63
Assessment of CE by *C*

PERIOD FOR SUBMISSION

62.3
The *C* submits quotations within three weeks of being instructed to do so by the *SM*

EXTENSION OF PERIOD

62.5
The *SM* extends the time allowed for
• the *C* to submit quotations for a CE and
• the *SM* to reply to a quotation

62.5
Does the *SM* and the *C* agree to extend the time allowed?

YES / NO

62.5
The *SM* notifies the extension that has been agreed to *C*

FC 13
Notification

SERVICE MANAGER ASSESSES

B
Sheet 2

62.3
Does the *C* submit quotations within the period for submission?

NO / YES

FC 13
C's submission

C
Sheet 2

QUOTATION SUBMITTED

Has the *C* submitted a quotation to the *SM?*

YES / NO

Finish

REVISED QUOTATION

FC 63
SM reviews *C*'s assessment of CE

REVIEW QUOTATION

SERVICE MANAGER'S REPLY

62.3
The *SM* replies within two weeks of the submission

EXTENSION OF PERIOD

62.5
The *SM* extends the time allowed for
• the *C* to submit quotations for a CE and
• the *SM* to reply to a quotation

SERVICE MANAGER REPLIES

62.5
Does the *SM* and the *C* agree to extend the time allowed?

YES / NO

A
Sheet 2

62.5
The *SM* notifies the extension that has been agreed to the *C*

FC 13
Notification

**Flow chart 62 Sheet 1 of 2
Quotations for compensation events**

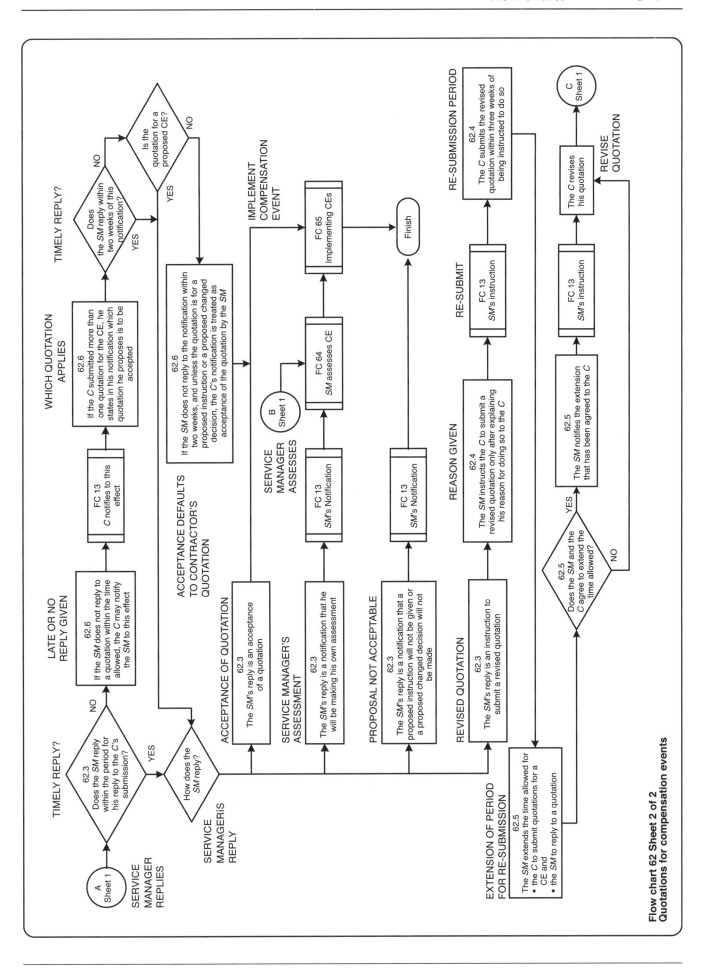

Flow chart 62 Sheet 2 of 2
Quotations for compensation events

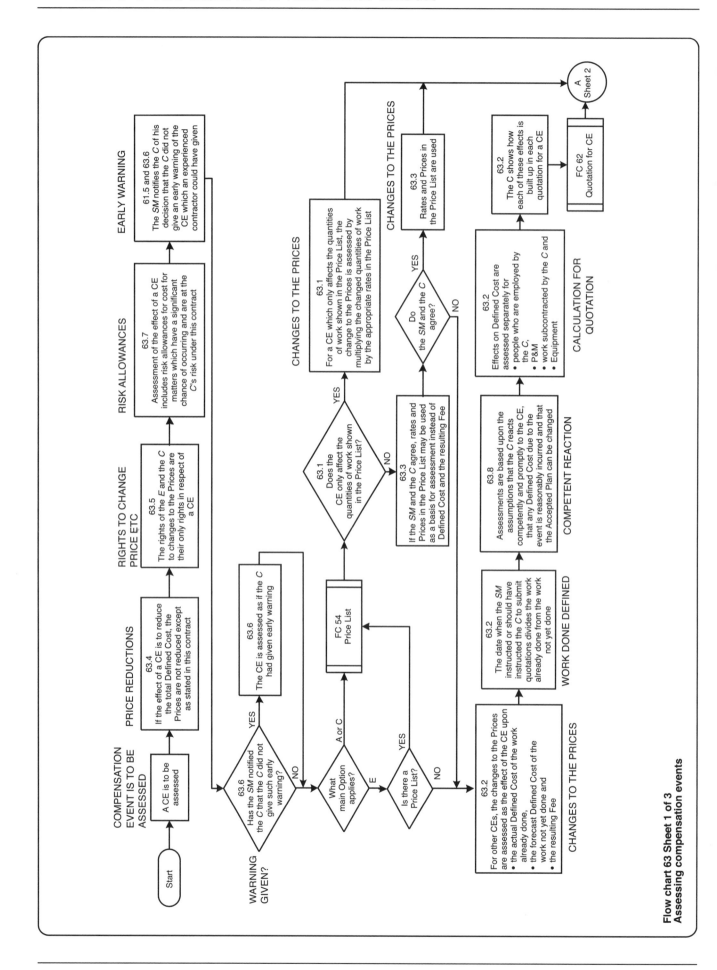

Flow chart 63 Sheet 1 of 3
Assessing compensation events

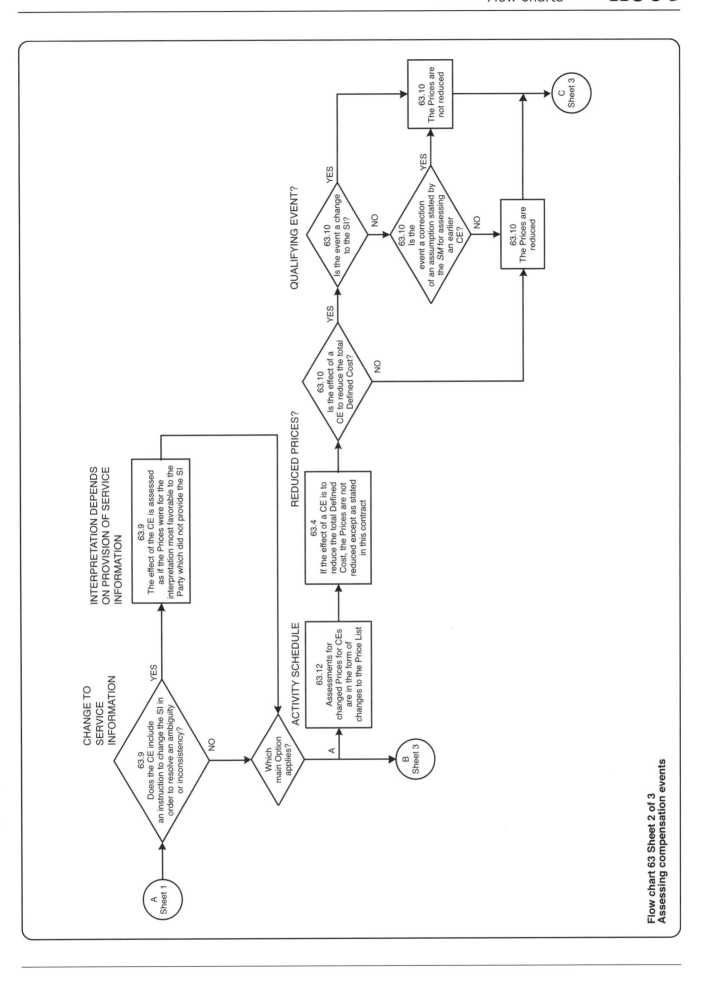

CHANGE TO SERVICE INFORMATION

63.9
Does the CE include an instruction to change the SI in order to resolve an ambiguity or inconsistency?

YES

INTERPRETATION DEPENDS ON PROVISION OF SERVICE INFORMATION

63.9
The effect of the CE is assessed as if the Prices were for the interpretation most favorable to the Party which did not provide the SI

NO

Which main Option applies?

A

ACTIVITY SCHEDULE

63.12
Assessments for changed Prices for CEs are in the form of changes to the Price List

B
Sheet 3

REDUCED PRICES?

63.4
If the effect of a CE is to reduce the total Defined Cost, the Prices are not reduced except as stated in this contract

63.10
Is the effect of a CE to reduce the total Defined Cost?

YES

NO

QUALIFYING EVENT?

63.10
Is the event a change to the SI?

YES

NO

63.10
Is the event a correction of an assumption stated by the SM for assessing an earlier CE?

YES

NO

63.10
The Prices are not reduced

63.10
The Prices are reduced

C
Sheet 3

A
Sheet 1

Flow chart 63 Sheet 2 of 3
Assessing compensation events

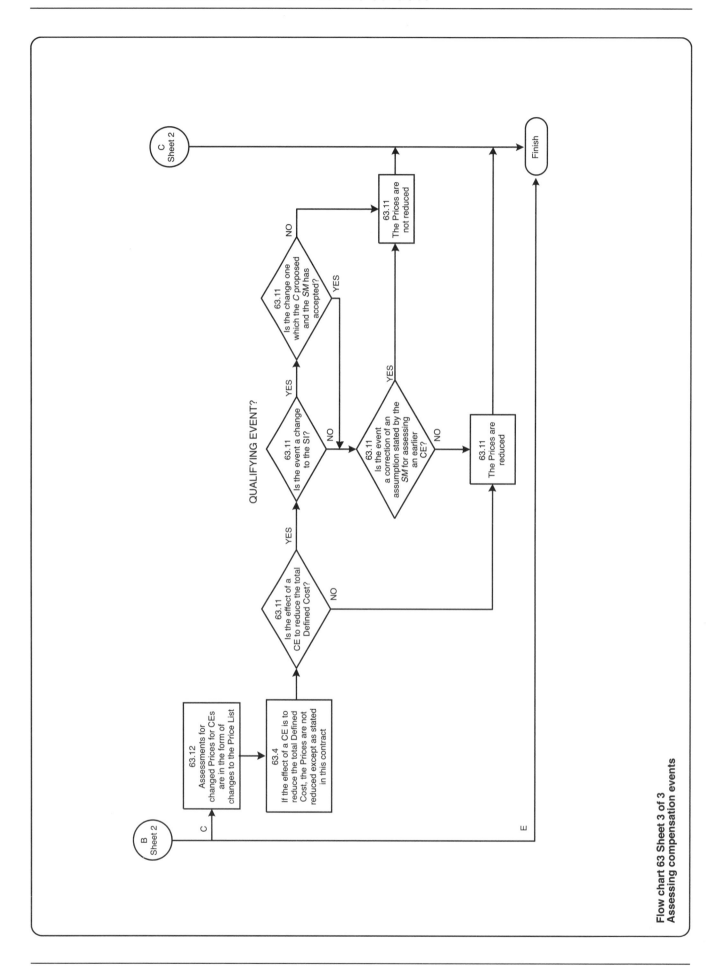

QUALIFYING EVENT?

63.12
Assessments for changed Prices for CEs are in the form of changes to the Price List

63.4
If the effect of a CE is to reduce the total Defined Cost, the Prices are not reduced except as stated in this contract

63.11
Is the effect of a CE to reduce the total Defined Cost?

63.11
Is the event a change to the SI?

63.11
Is the change one which the C proposed and the SM has accepted?

63.11
Is the event a correction of an assumption stated by the SM for assessing an earlier CE?

63.11
The Prices are not reduced

63.11
The Prices are reduced

B
Sheet 2

C
Sheet 2

Finish

**Flow chart 63 Sheet 3 of 3
Assessing compensation events**

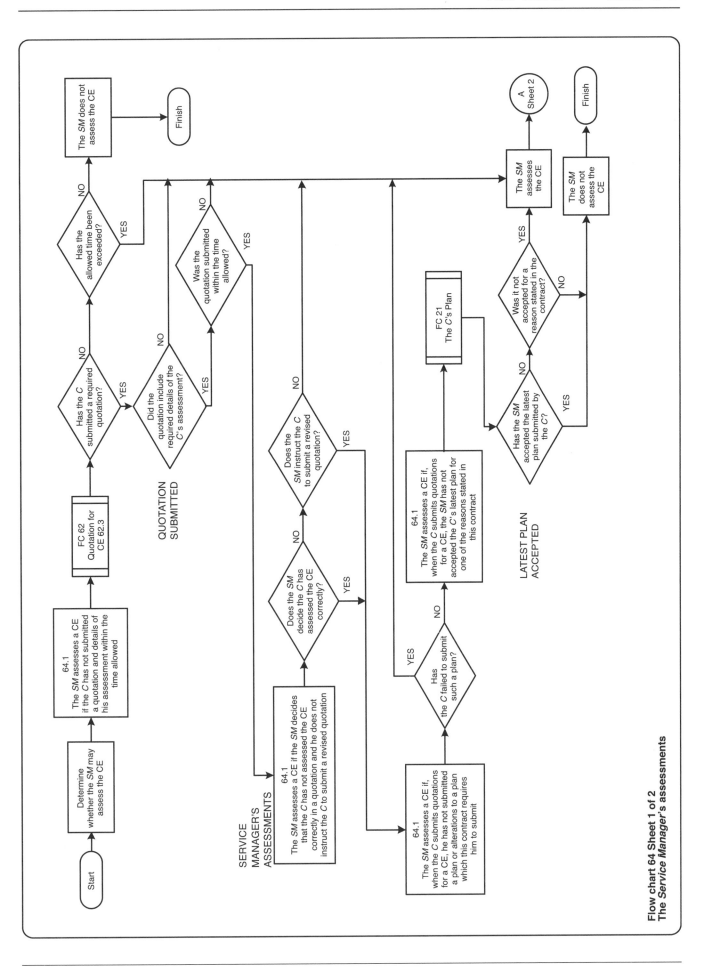

Flow chart 64 Sheet 1 of 2
The *Service Manager's* assessments

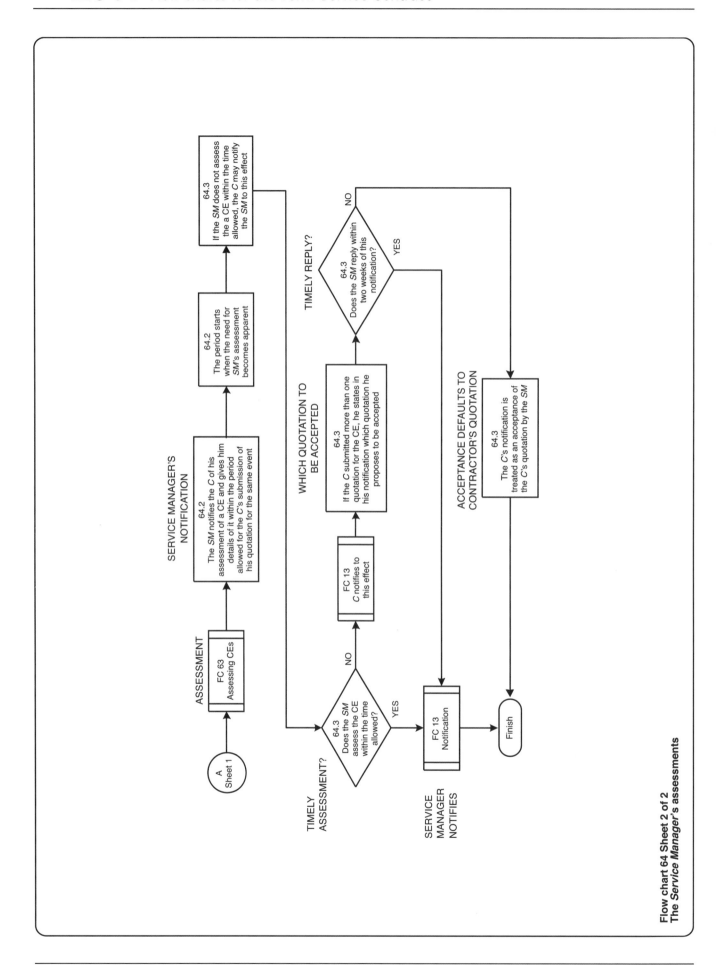

Flow chart 64 Sheet 2 of 2
The *Service Manager*'s assessments

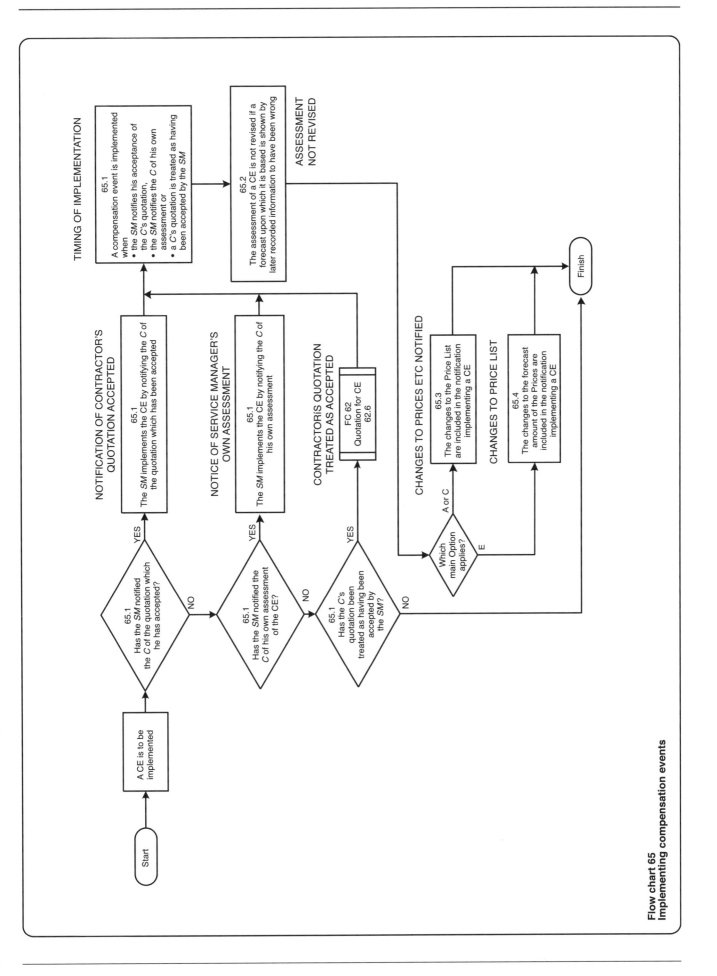

TIMING OF IMPLEMENTATION

65.1
A compensation event is implemented when
• the *SM* notifies his acceptance of the *C*'s quotation,
• the *SM* notifies the *C* of his own assessment or
• a *C*'s quotation is treated as having been accepted by the *SM*

65.2
The assessment of a CE is not revised if a forecast upon which it is based is shown by later recorded information to have been wrong

ASSESSMENT NOT REVISED

NOTIFICATION OF CONTRACTOR'S QUOTATION ACCEPTED

65.1
The *SM* implements the CE by notifying the *C* of the quotation which has been accepted

NOTICE OF SERVICE MANAGER'S OWN ASSESSMENT

65.1
The *SM* implements the CE by notifying the *C* of his own assessment

CONTRACTOR'S QUOTATION TREATED AS ACCEPTED

FC 62
Quotation for CE
62.6

CHANGES TO PRICES ETC NOTIFIED

65.3
The changes to the Price List are included in the notification implementing a CE

CHANGES TO PRICE LIST

65.4
The changes to the forecast amount of the Prices are included in the notification implementing a CE

Finish

65.1
Has the *SM* notified the *C* of the quotation which he has accepted?

YES / NO

65.1
Has the *SM* notified the *C* of his own assessment of the CE?

YES / NO

65.1
Has the *C*'s quotation been treated as having been accepted by the *SM*?

YES / NO

Which main Option applies?

A or C / E

A CE is to be implemented

Start

**Flow chart 65
Implementing compensation events**

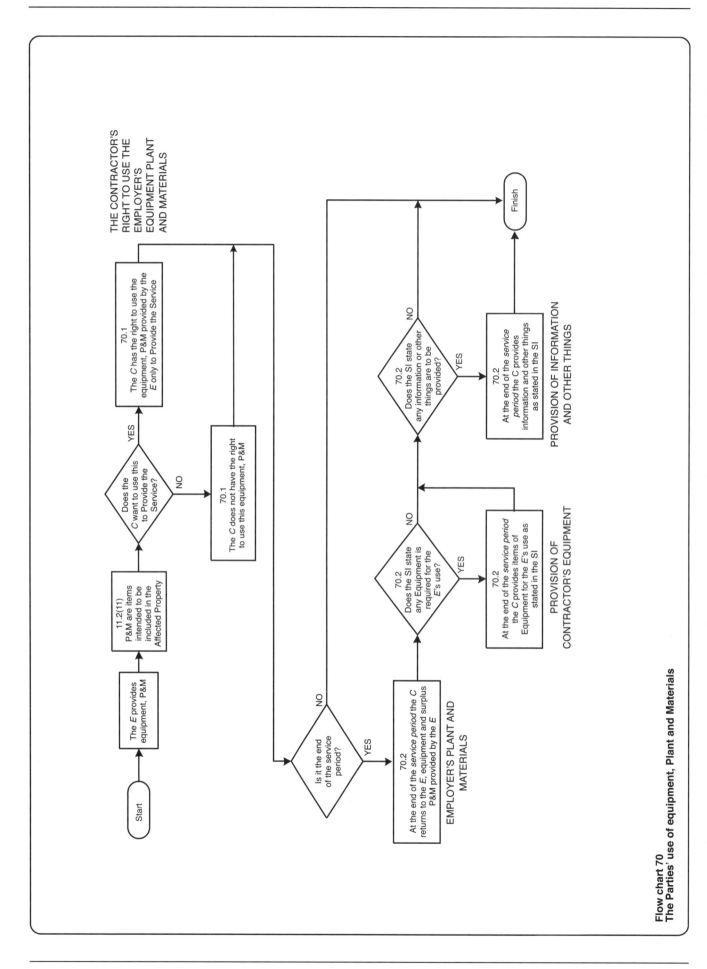

Flow chart 70
The Parties' use of equipment, Plant and Materials

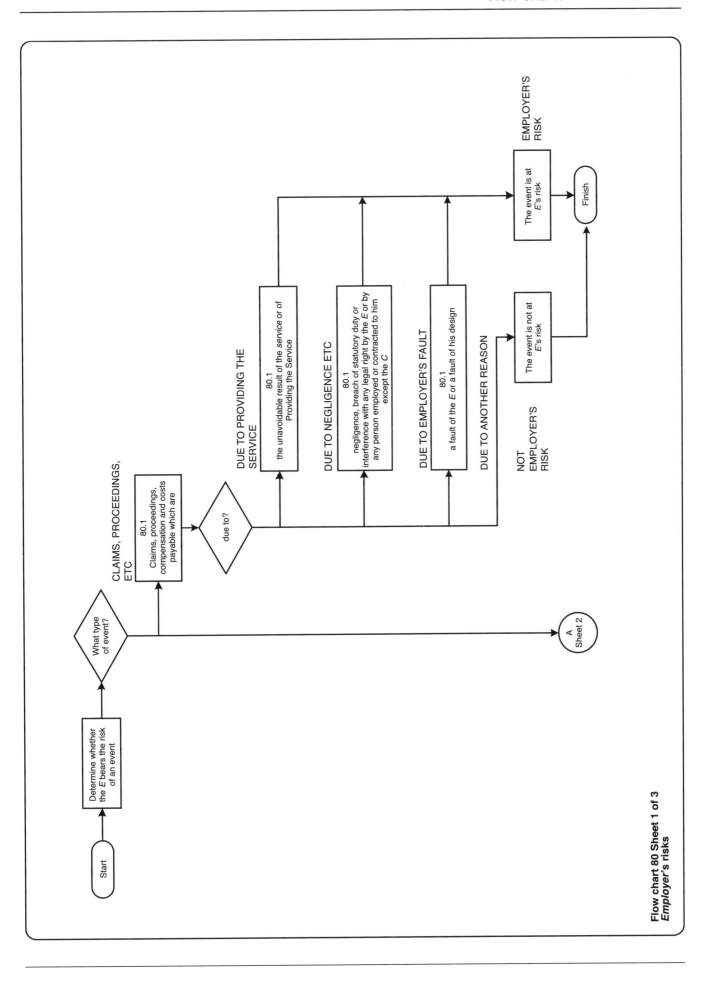

Flow chart 80 Sheet 1 of 3
Employer's risks

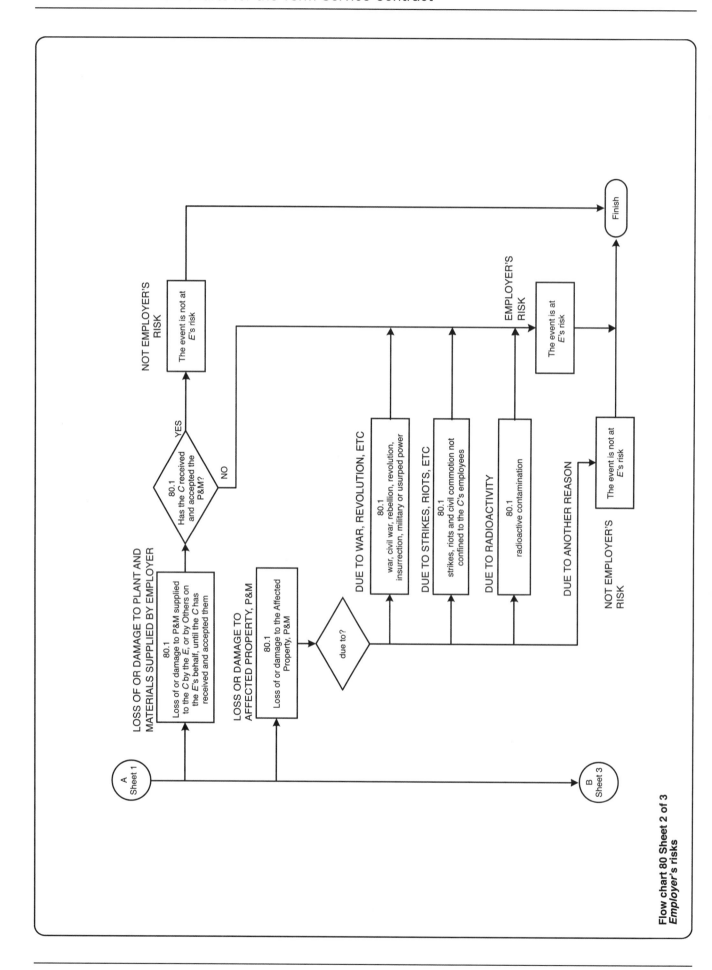

Flow chart 80 Sheet 2 of 3
Employer's risks

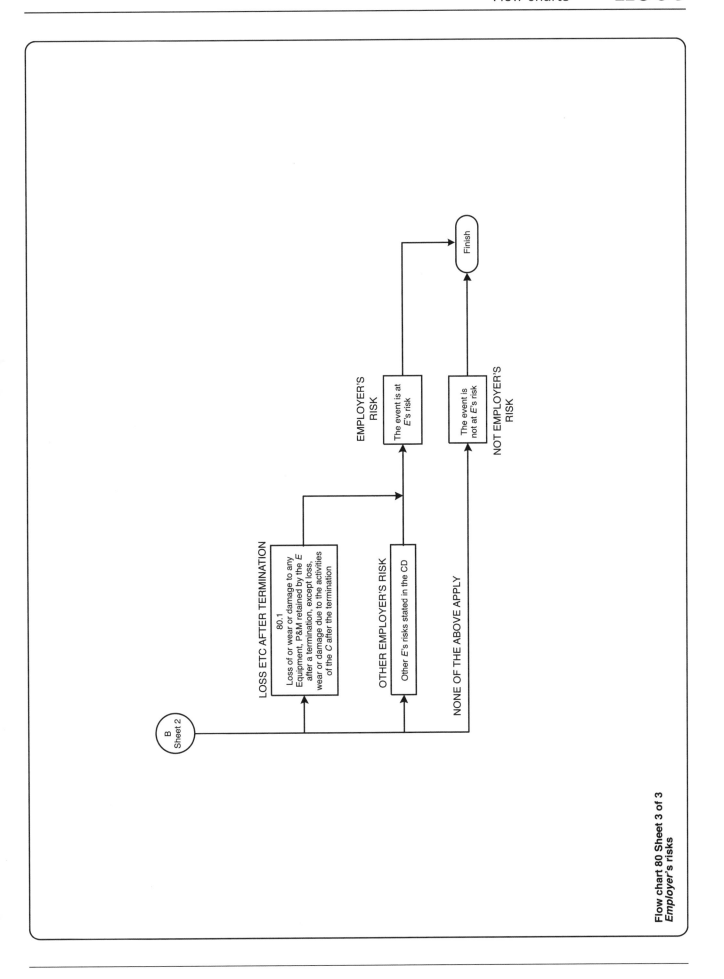

Flow chart 80 Sheet 3 of 3
Employer's risks

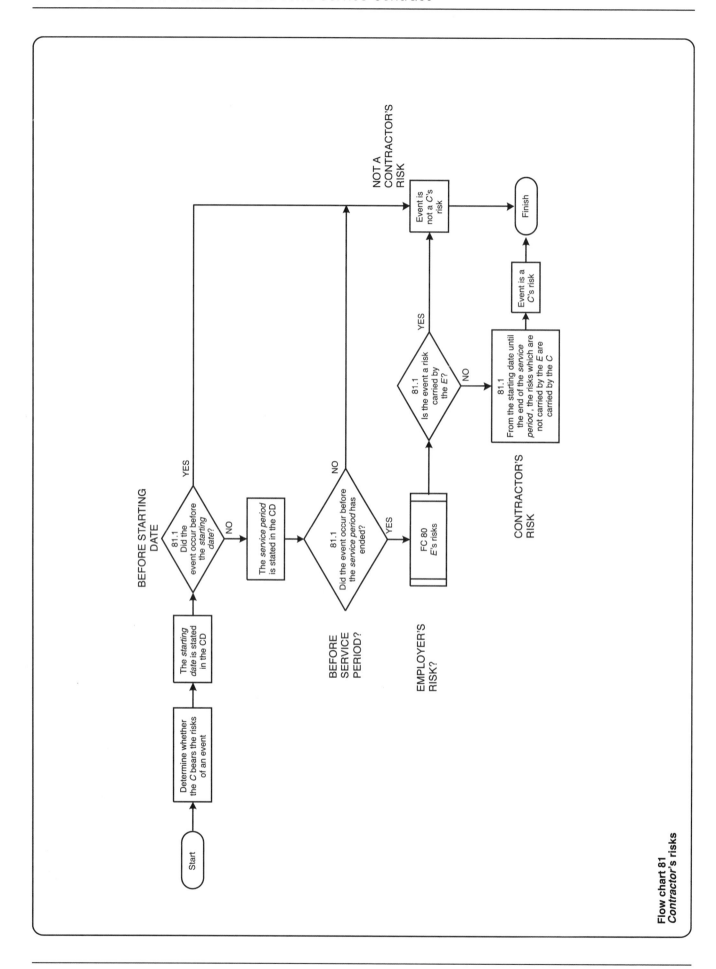

Flow chart 81
Contractor's risks

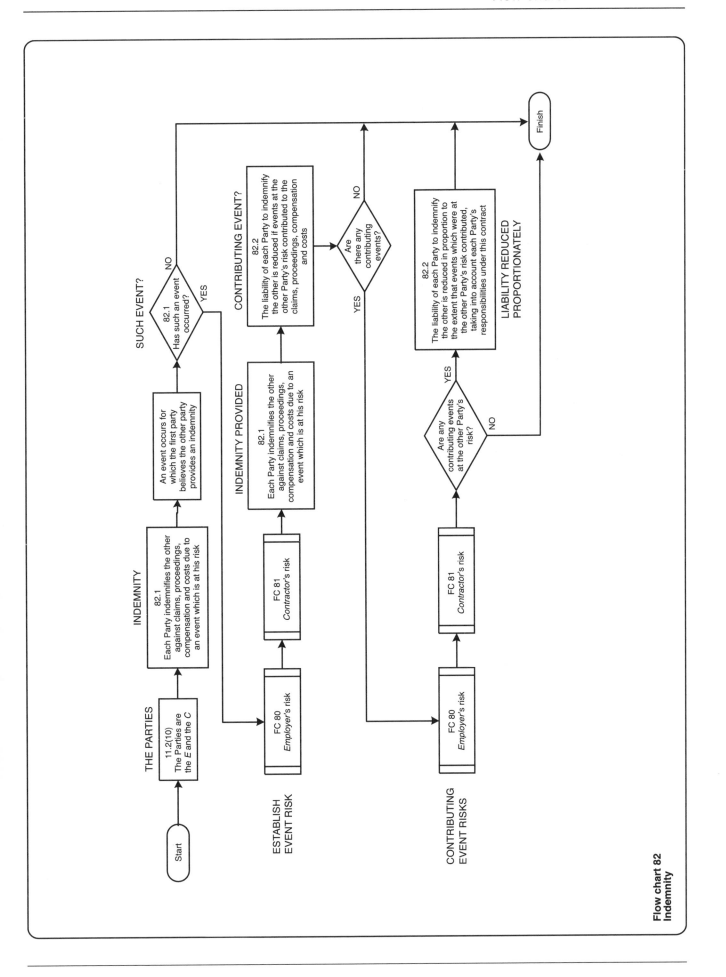

Flow chart 82
Indemnity

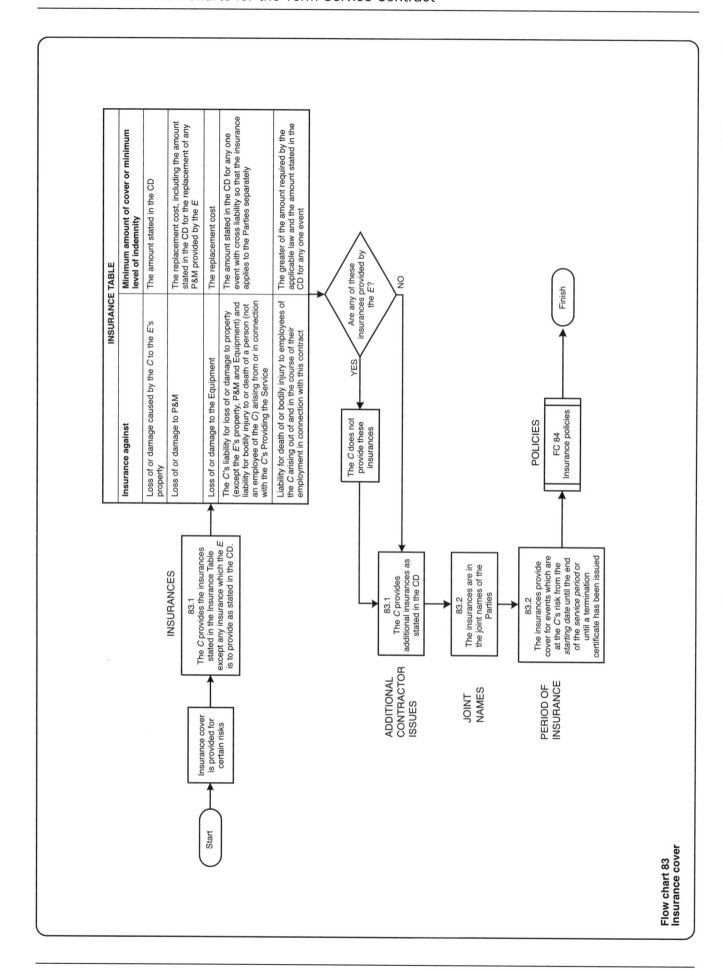

INSURANCE TABLE

Insurance against	Minimum amount of cover or minimum level of indemnity
Loss of or damage caused by the *C* to the *E*'s property	The amount stated in the CD
Loss of or damage to P&M	The replacement cost, including the amount stated in the CD for the replacement of any P&M provided by the *E*
Loss of or damage to the Equipment	The replacement cost
The *C*'s liability for loss of or damage to property (except the *E*'s property, P&M and Equipment) and liability for bodily injury to or death of a person (not an employee of the *C*) arising from or in connection with the *C*'s Providing the Service	The amount stated in the CD for any one event with cross liability so that the insurance applies to the Parties separately
Liability for death of or bodily injury to employees of the *C* arising out of and in the course of their employment in connection with this contract	The greater of the amount required by the applicable law and the amount stated in the CD for any one event

INSURANCES

Start

Insurance cover is provided for certain risks

83.1
The *C* provides the insurances stated in the Insurance Table except any insurance which the *E* is to provide as stated in the CD.

Are any of these insurances provided by the *E*?

YES — The *C* does not provide these insurances

NO

ADDITIONAL CONTRACTOR ISSUES

83.1
The *C* provides additional insurances as stated in the CD

JOINT NAMES

83.2
The insurances are in the joint names of the Parties

PERIOD OF INSURANCE

83.2
The insurances provide cover for events which are at the *C*'s risk from the *starting date* until the end of the *service period* or until a termination certificate has been issued

POLICIES

FC 84
Insurance policies

Finish

Flow chart 83
Insurance cover

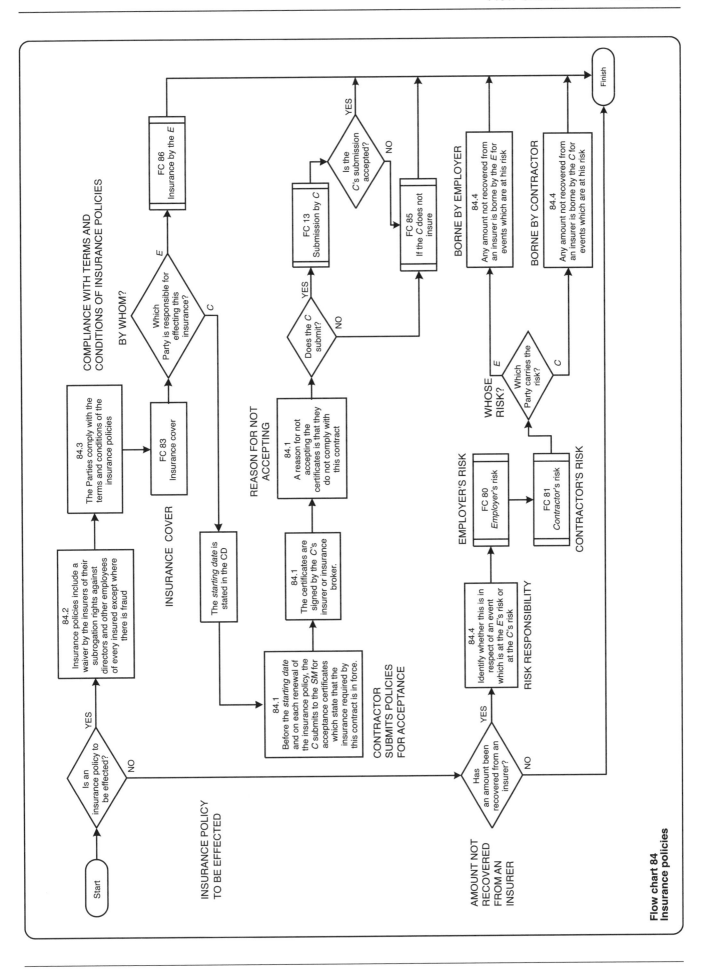

Flow chart 84
Insurance policies

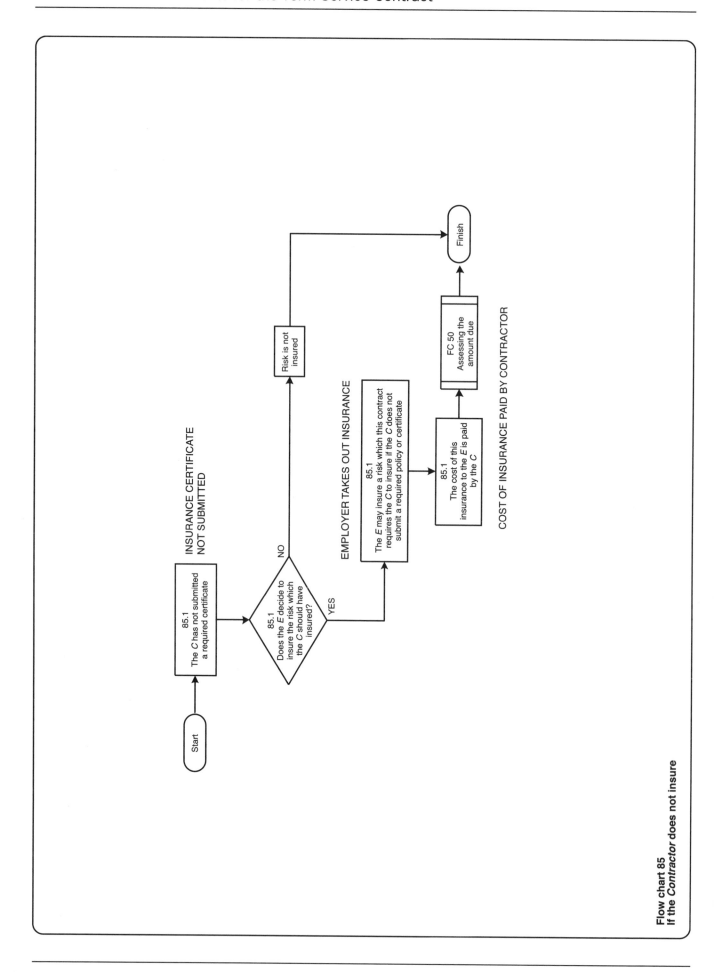

INSURANCE CERTIFICATE
NOT SUBMITTED

Start

85.1
The C has not submitted
a required certificate

85.1
Does the E decide to
insure the risk which
the C should have
insured?

NO

YES

Risk is not
insured

Finish

EMPLOYER TAKES OUT INSURANCE

85.1
The E may insure a risk which this contract
requires the C to insure if the C does not
submit a required policy or certificate

85.1
The cost of this
insurance to the E is paid
by the C

FC 50
Assessing the
amount due

COST OF INSURANCE PAID BY CONTRACTOR

Flow chart 85
If the *Contractor* does not insure

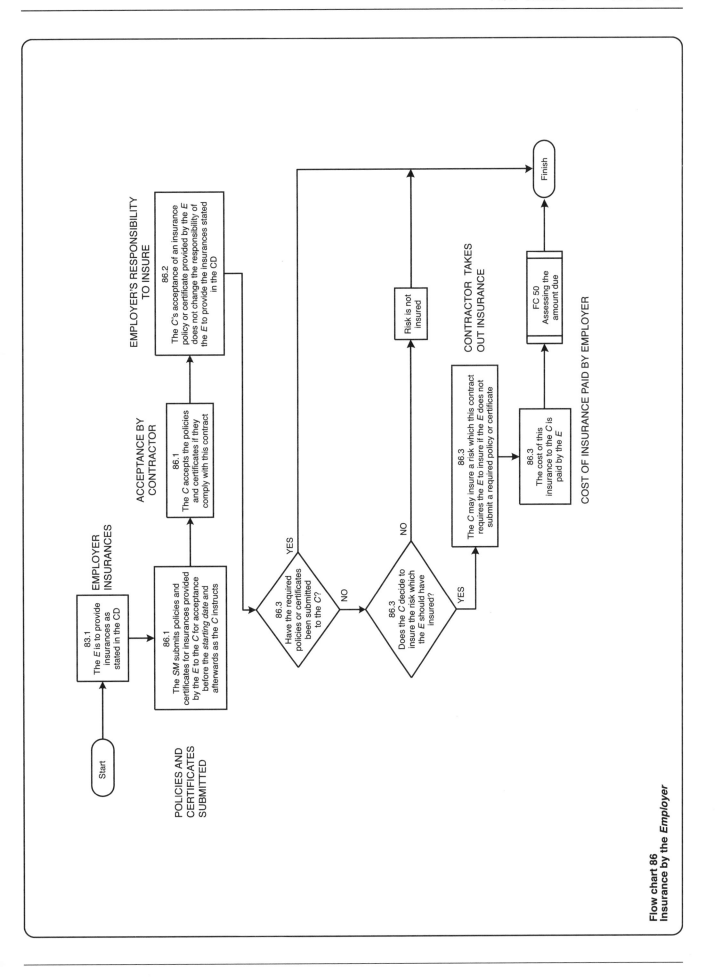

Flow chart 86
Insurance by the *Employer*

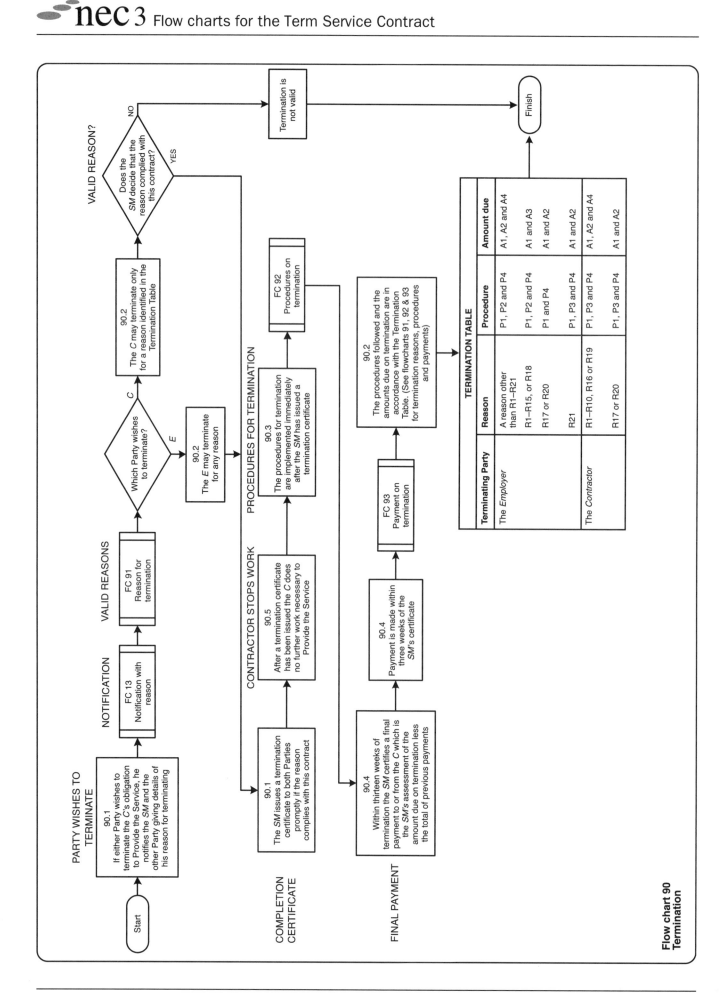

**Flow chart 90
Termination**

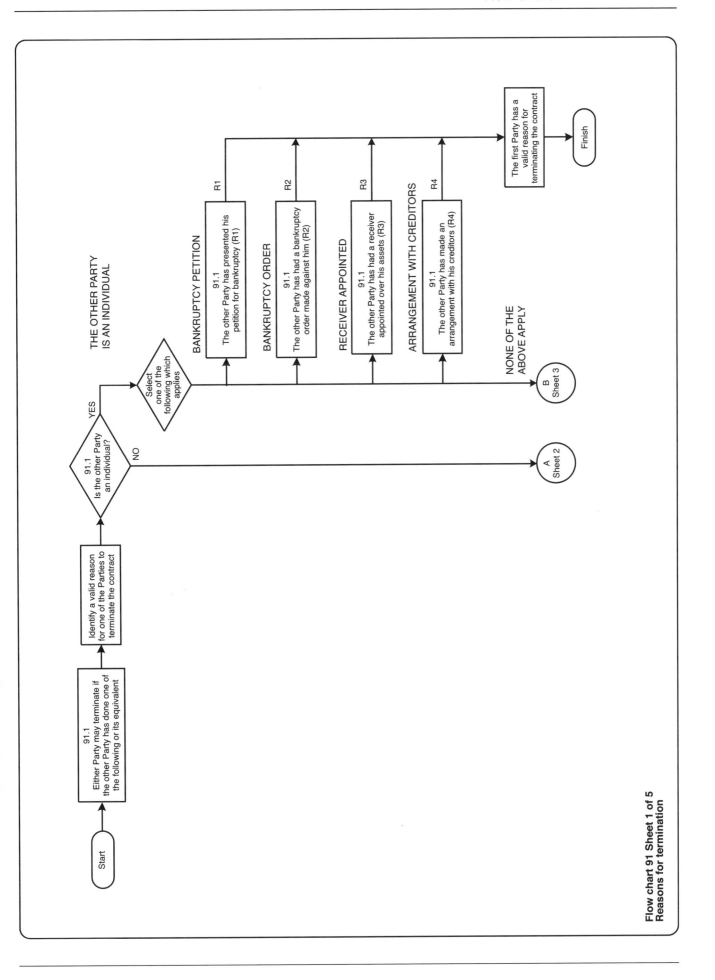

Flow chart 91 Sheet 1 of 5
Reasons for termination

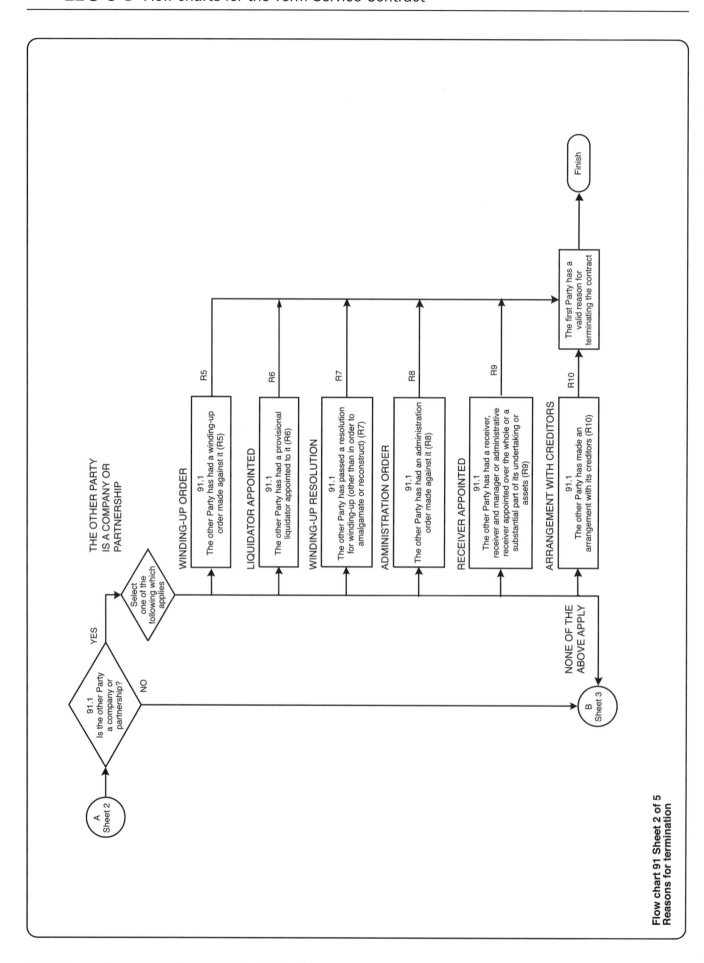

Flow chart 91 Sheet 2 of 5
Reasons for termination

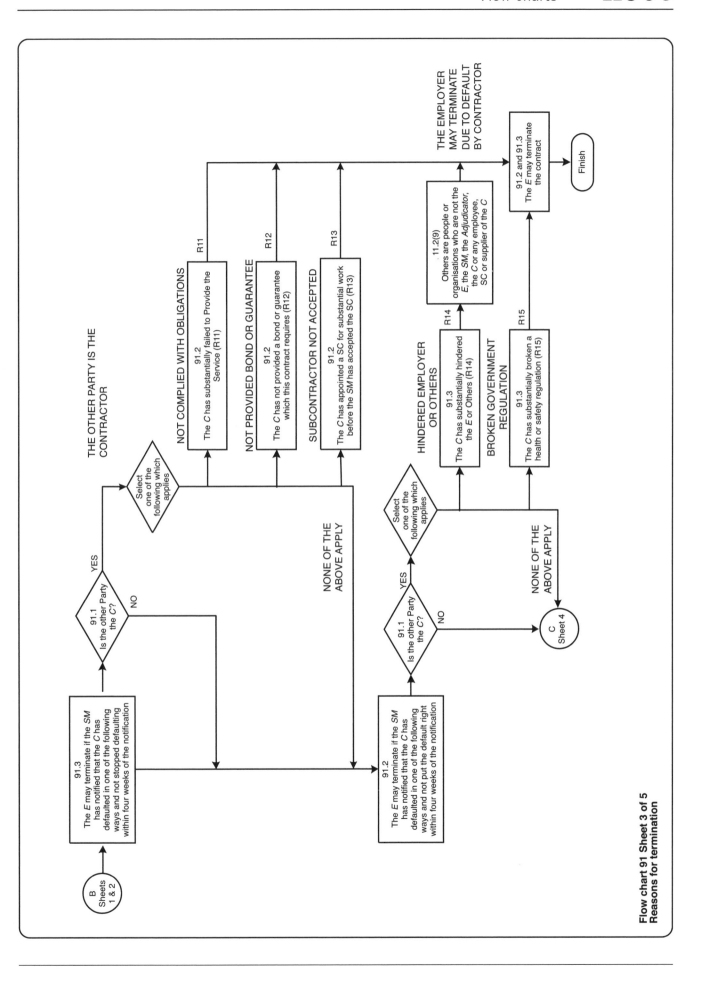

Flow chart 91 Sheet 3 of 5
Reasons for termination

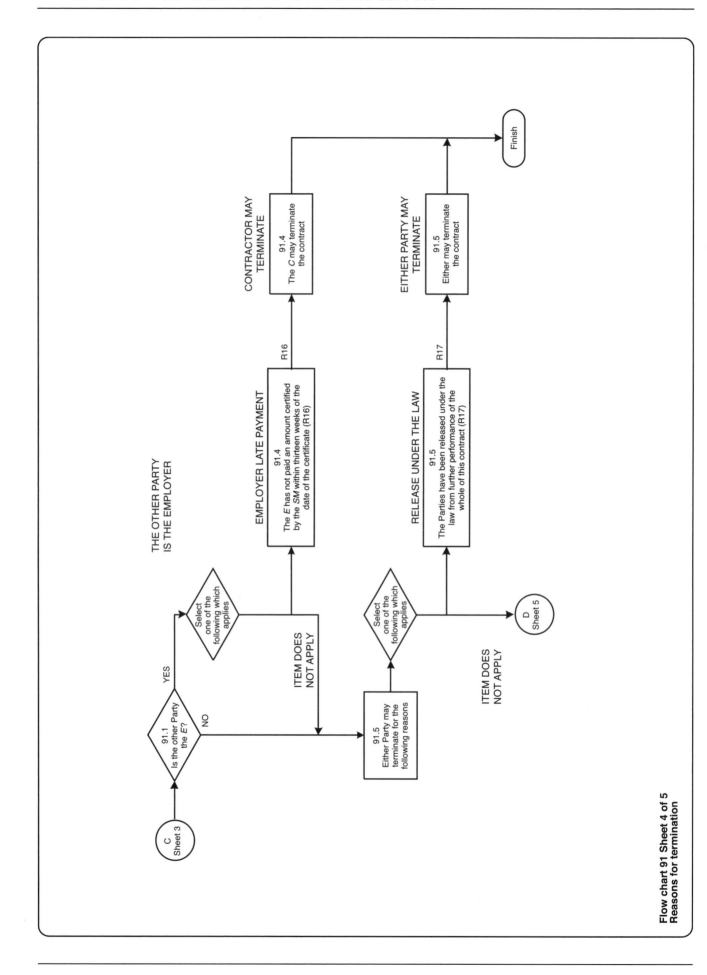

Flow chart 91 Sheet 4 of 5
Reasons for termination

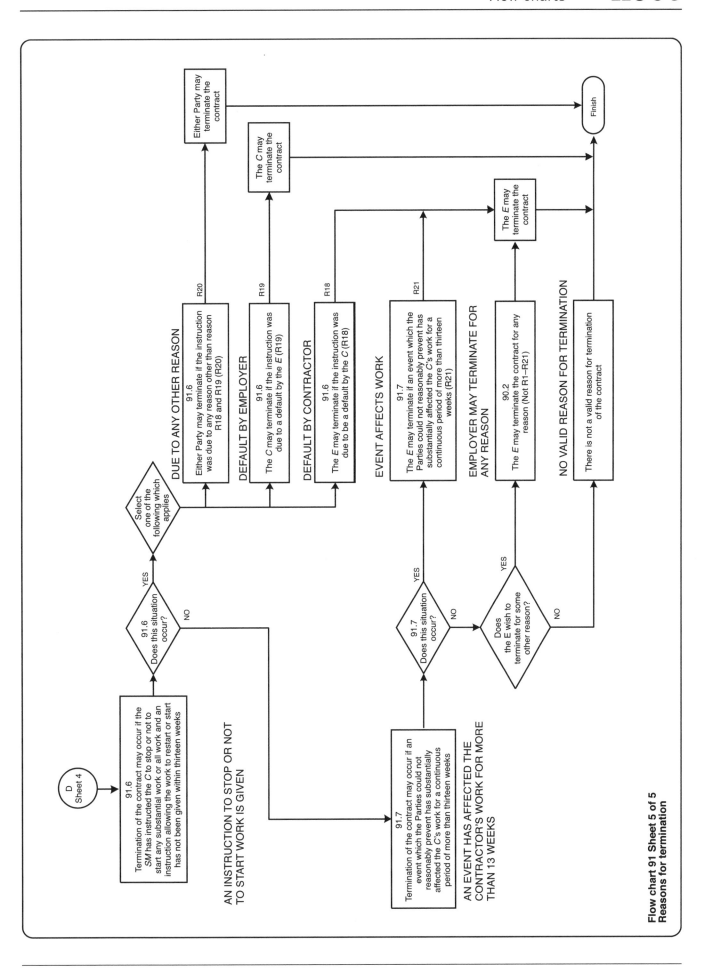

Flow chart 91 Sheet 5 of 5
Reasons for termination

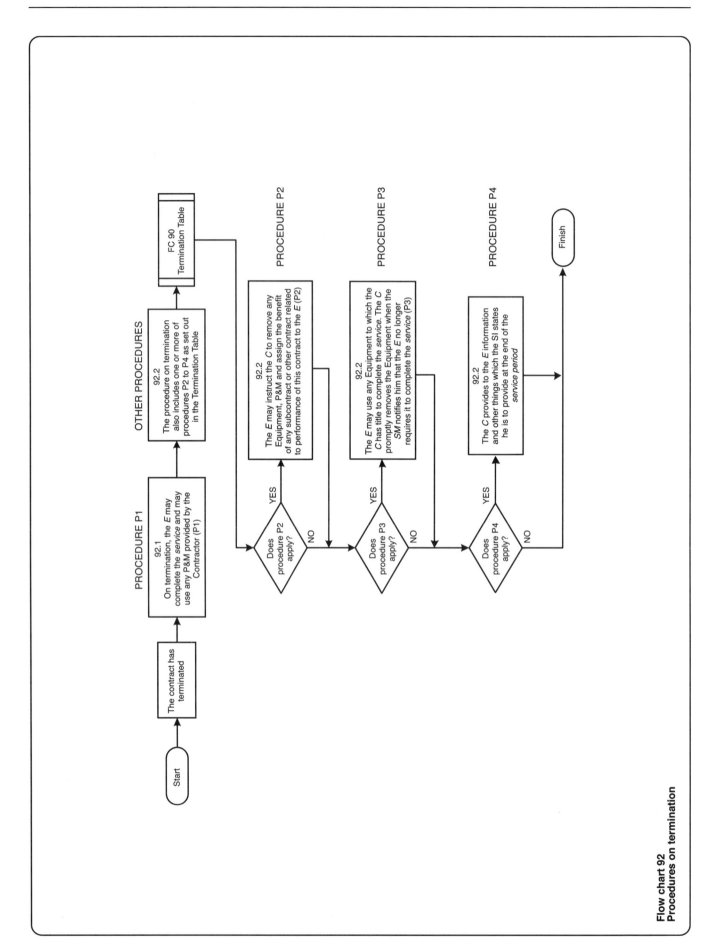

Flow chart 92
Procedures on termination

nec 3

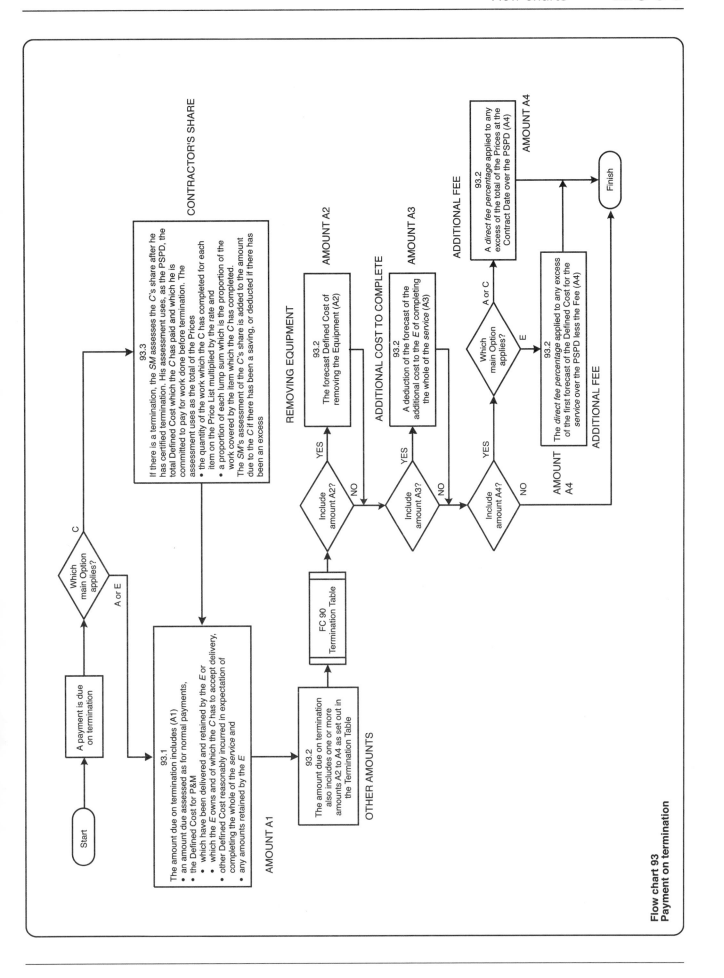

Flow chart 93
Payment on termination

© copyright nec 2005   73

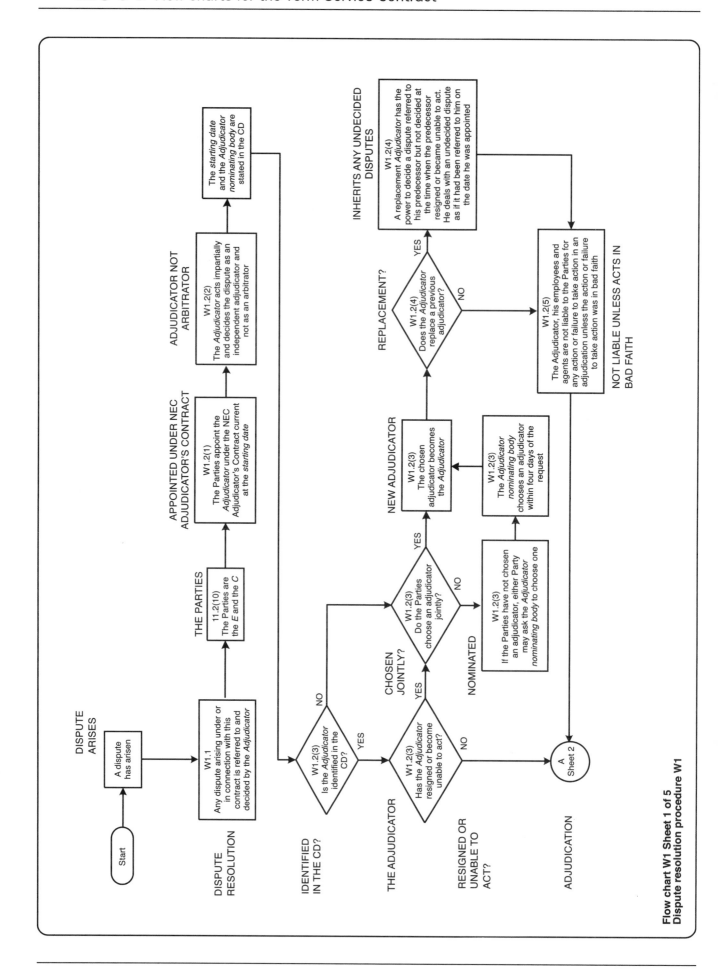
DISPUTE ARISES

Start

A dispute has arisen

DISPUTE RESOLUTION

W1.1
Any dispute arising under or in connection with this contract is referred to and decided by the *Adjudicator*

THE PARTIES

11.2(10)
The Parties are the *E* and the *C*

APPOINTED UNDER NEC ADJUDICATOR'S CONTRACT

W1.2(1)
The Parties appoint the *Adjudicator* under the NEC Adjudicator's Contract current at the *starting date*

ADJUDICATOR NOT ARBITRATOR

W1.2(2)
The *Adjudicator* acts impartially and decides the dispute as an independent adjudicator and not as an arbitrator

The *starting date* and the *Adjudicator nominating body* are stated in the CD

IDENTIFIED IN THE CD?

W1.2(3)
Is the *Adjudicator* identified in the CD?

NO

YES

THE ADJUDICATOR

W1.2(3)
Has the *Adjudicator* resigned or become unable to act?

YES

NO

RESIGNED OR UNABLE TO ACT?

CHOSEN JOINTLY?

W1.2(3)
Do the Parties choose an adjudicator jointly?

YES

NO

NOMINATED

W1.2(3)
If the Parties have not chosen an adjudicator, either Party may ask the *Adjudicator nominating body* to choose one

W1.2(3)
The *Adjudicator nominating body* chooses an adjudicator within four days of the request

NEW ADJUDICATOR

W1.2(3)
The chosen adjudicator becomes the *Adjudicator*

REPLACEMENT?

W1.2(4)
Does the *Adjudicator* replace a previous adjudicator?

YES

NO

INHERITS ANY UNDECIDED DISPUTES

W1.2(4)
A replacement *Adjudicator* has the power to decide a dispute referred to his predecessor but not decided at the time when the predecessor resigned or became unable to act. He deals with an undecided dispute as if it had been referred to him on the date he was appointed

W1.2(5)
The Adjudicator, his employees and agents are not liable to the Parties for any action or failure to take action in an adjudication unless the action or failure to take action was in bad faith

NOT LIABLE UNLESS ACTS IN BAD FAITH

ADJUDICATION

A
Sheet 2

Flow chart W1 Sheet 1 of 5
Dispute resolution procedure W1

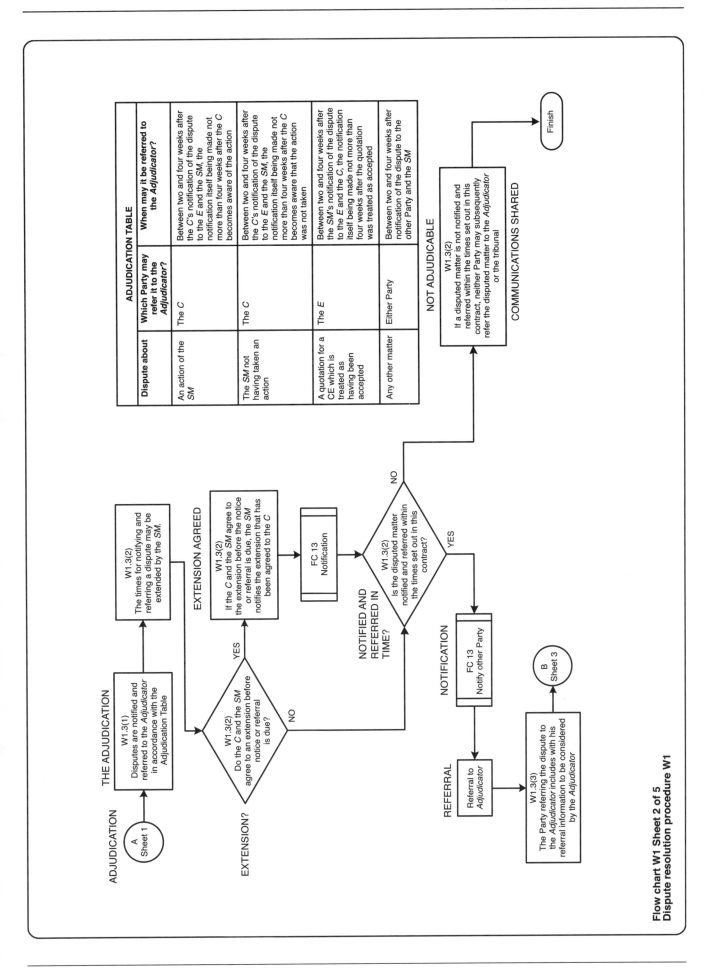

ADJUDICATION TABLE

Dispute about	Which Party may refer it to the *Adjudicator*?	When may it be referred to the *Adjudicator*?
An action of the *SM*	The *C*	Between two and four weeks after the *C*'s notification of the dispute to the *E* and the *SM*, the notification itself being made not more than four weeks after the *C* becomes aware of the action
The *SM* not having taken an action	The *C*	Between two and four weeks after the *C*'s notification of the dispute to the *E* and the *SM*, the notification itself being made not more than four weeks after the *C* becomes aware that the action was not taken
A quotation for a CE which is treated as having been accepted	The *E*	Between two and four weeks after the *SM*'s notification of the dispute to the *E* and the *C*, the notification itself being made not more than four weeks after the quotation was treated as accepted
Any other matter	Either Party	Between two and four weeks after notification of the dispute to the other Party and the *SM*

ADJUDICATION

THE ADJUDICATION

A Sheet 1

W1.3(1)
Disputes are notified and referred to the *Adjudicator* in accordance with the Adjudication Table

W1.3(2)
The times for notifying and referring a dispute may be extended by the *SM*.

EXTENSION?

W1.3(2)
Do the *C* and the *SM* agree to an extension before notice or referral is due?

EXTENSION AGREED

YES

W1.3(2)
If the *C* and the *SM* agree to the extension before the notice or referral is due, the *SM* notifies the extension that has been agreed to the *C*

NO

FC 13
Notification

NOTIFIED AND REFERRED IN TIME?

W1.3(2)
Is the disputed matter notified and referred within the times set out in this contract?

NO

NOT ADJUDICABLE

W1.3(2)
If a disputed matter is not notified and referred within the times set out in this contract, neither Party may subsequently refer the disputed matter to the *Adjudicator* or the tribunal

COMMUNICATIONS SHARED

Finish

YES

NOTIFICATION

FC 13
Notify other Party

REFERRAL

Referral to *Adjudicator*

W1.3(3)
The Party referring the dispute to the *Adjudicator* includes with his referral information to be considered by the *Adjudicator*

B Sheet 3

**Flow chart W1 Sheet 2 of 5
Dispute resolution procedure W1**

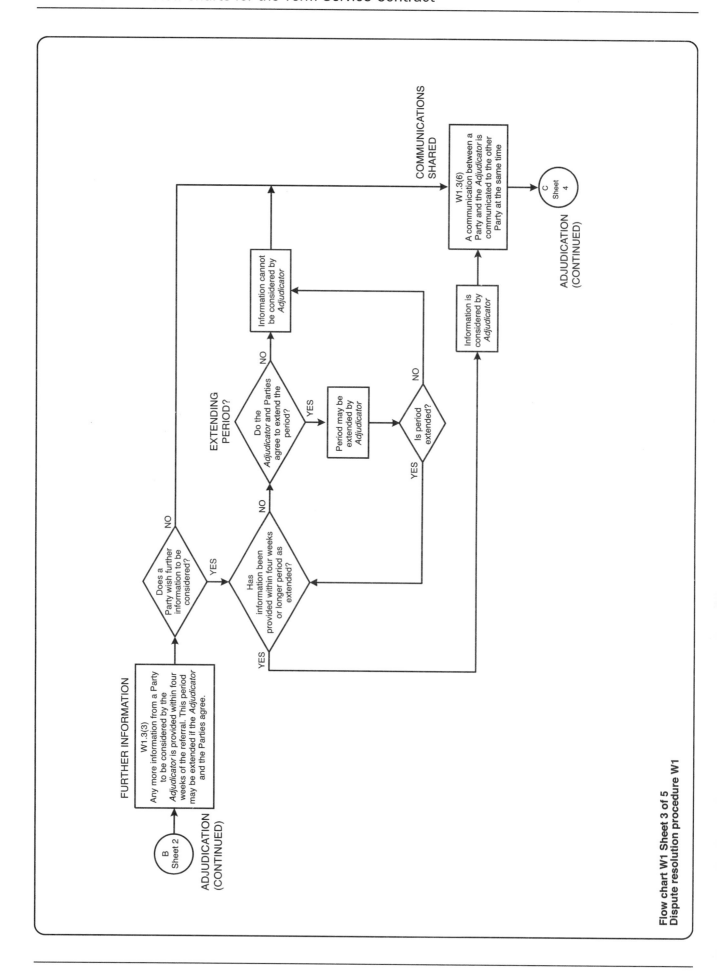

FURTHER INFORMATION

W1.3(3)
Any more information from a Party to be considered by the *Adjudicator* is provided within four weeks of the referral. This period may be extended if the *Adjudicator* and the Parties agree.

B
Sheet 2

ADJUDICATION (CONTINUED)

Does a Party wish further information to be considered?

EXTENDING PERIOD?

Has information been provided within four weeks or longer period as extended?

Do the *Adjudicator* and Parties agree to extend the period?

Information cannot be considered by *Adjudicator*

Period may be extended by *Adjudicator*

Is period extended?

Information is considered by *Adjudicator*

COMMUNICATIONS SHARED

W1.3(6)
A communication between a Party and the *Adjudicator* is communicated to the other Party at the same time

C
Sheet 4

ADJUDICATION (CONTINUED)

Flow chart W1 Sheet 3 of 5
Dispute resolution procedure W1

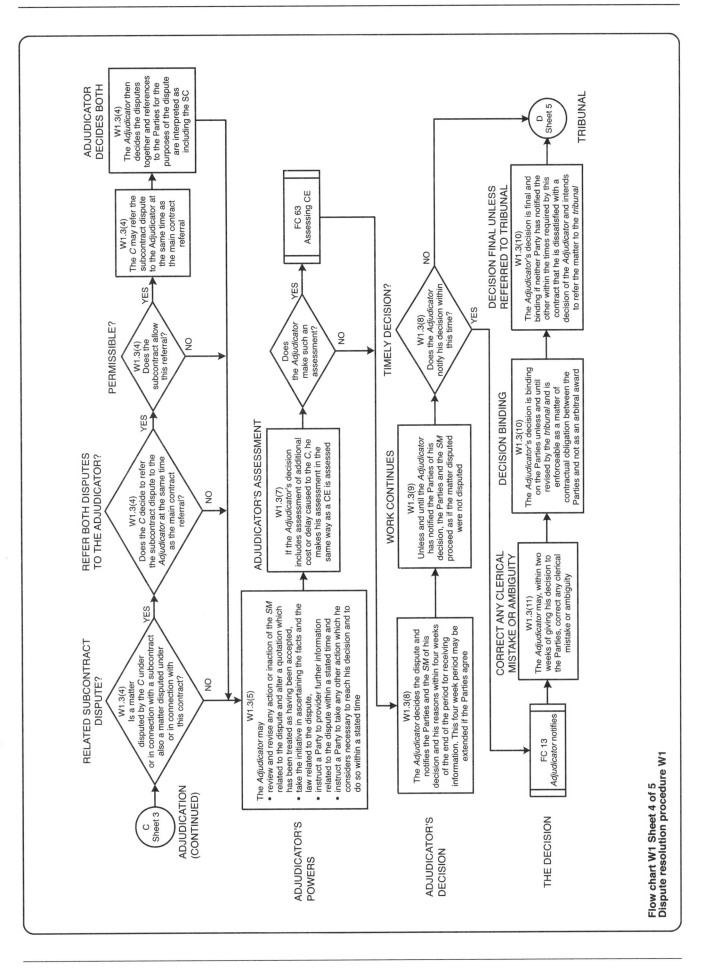

RELATED SUBCONTRACT DISPUTE?

W1.3(4)
Is a matter disputed by the *C* under or in connection with a subcontract also a matter disputed under or in connection with this contract?

REFER BOTH DISPUTES TO THE ADJUDICATOR?

W1.3(4)
Does the *C* decide to refer the subcontract dispute to the *Adjudicator* at the same time as the main contract referral?

PERMISSIBLE?

W1.3(4)
Does the subcontract allow this referral?

W1.3(4)
The *C* may refer the subcontract dispute to the Adjudicator at the same time as the main contract referral

ADJUDICATOR DECIDES BOTH

W1.3(4)
The *Adjudicator* then decides the disputes together and references to the Parties for the purposes of the dispute are interpreted as including the SC

ADJUDICATION (CONTINUED)

C
Sheet 3

ADJUDICATOR'S POWERS

W1.3(5)
The *Adjudicator* may
• review and revise any action or inaction of the *SM* related to the dispute and alter a quotation which has been treated as having been accepted,
• take the initiative in ascertaining the facts and the law related to the dispute,
• instruct a Party to provider further information related to the dispute within a stated time and
• instruct a Party to take any other action which he considers necessary to reach his decision and to do so within a stated time

ADJUDICATOR'S ASSESSMENT

W1.3(7)
If the *Adjudicator's* decision includes assessment of additional cost or delay caused to the *C*, he makes his assessment in the same way as a CE is assessed

Does the *Adjudicator* make such an assessment?

YES

FC 63
Assessing CE

NO

ADJUDICATOR'S DECISION

W1.3(8)
The *Adjudicator* decides the dispute and notifies the Parties and the *SM* of his decision and his reasons within four weeks of the end of the period for receiving information. This four week period may be extended if the Parties agree

WORK CONTINUES

W1.3(9)
Unless and until the *Adjudicator* has notified the Parties of his decision, the Parties and the *SM* proceed as if the matter disputed were not disputed

TIMELY DECISION?

W1.3(8)
Does the *Adjudicator* notify his decision within this time?

NO

YES

CORRECT ANY CLERICAL MISTAKE OR AMBIGUITY

W1.3(11)
The *Adjudicator* may, within two weeks of giving his decision to the Parties, correct any clerical mistake or ambiguity

THE DECISION

FC 13
Adjudicator notifies

DECISION BINDING

W1.3(10)
The *Adjudicator's* decision is binding on the Parties unless and until revised by the *tribunal* and is enforceable as a matter of contractual obligation between the Parties and not as an arbitral award

DECISION FINAL UNLESS REFERRED TO TRIBUNAL

W1.3(10)
The *Adjudicator's* decision is final and binding if neither Party has notified the other within the times required by this contract that he is dissatisfied with a decision of the *Adjudicator* and intends to refer the matter to the *tribunal*

D
Sheet 5

TRIBUNAL

Flow chart W1 Sheet 4 of 5
Dispute resolution procedure W1

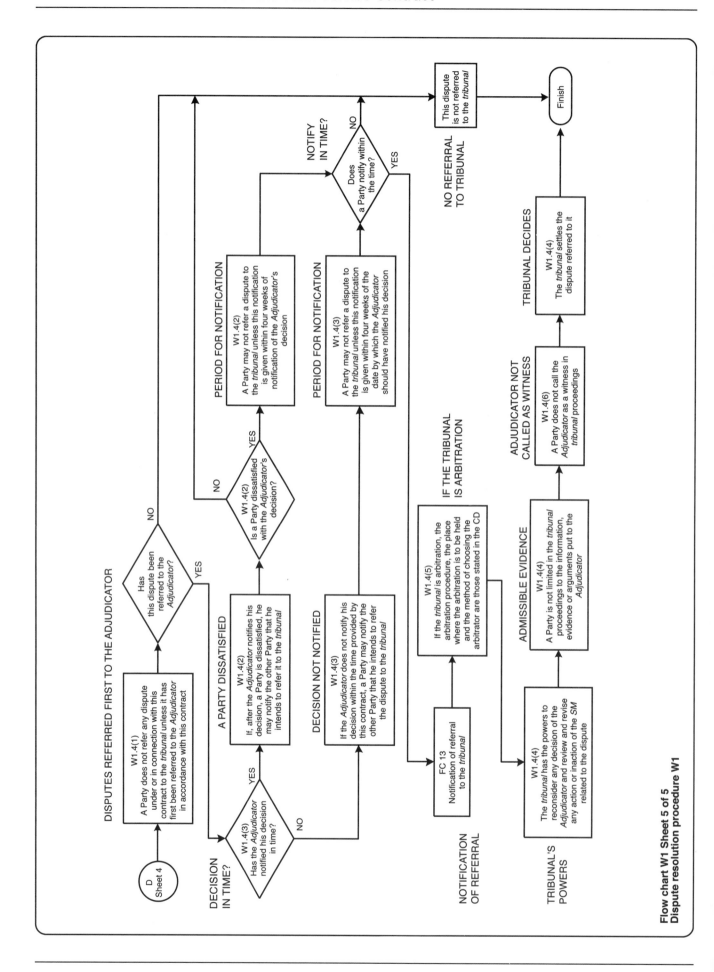

DISPUTES REFERRED FIRST TO THE ADJUDICATOR

D
Sheet 4

W1.4(1)
A Party does not refer any dispute under or in connection with this contract to the *tribunal* unless it has first been referred to the *Adjudicator* in accordance with this contract

Has this dispute been referred to the *Adjudicator*?

NO

YES

DECISION IN TIME?

W1.4(3)
Has the *Adjudicator* notified his decision in time?

YES

NO

A PARTY DISSATISFIED

W1.4(2)
If, after the *Adjudicator* notifies his decision, a Party is dissatisfied, he may notify the other Party that he intends to refer it to the *tribunal*

W1.4(2)
Is a Party dissatisfied with the *Adjudicator's* decision?

NO

YES

PERIOD FOR NOTIFICATION

W1.4(2)
A Party may not refer a dispute to the *tribunal* unless this notification is given within four weeks of notification of the *Adjudicator's* decision

DECISION NOT NOTIFIED

W1.4(3)
If the *Adjudicator* does not notify his decision within the time provided by this contract, a Party may notify the other Party that he intends to refer the dispute to the *tribunal*

PERIOD FOR NOTIFICATION

W1.4(3)
A Party may not refer a dispute to the *tribunal* unless this notification is given within four weeks of the date by which the *Adjudicator* should have notified his decision

NOTIFY IN TIME?

Does a Party notify within the time?

NO

YES

NO REFERRAL TO TRIBUNAL

This dispute is not referred to the *tribunal*

Finish

NOTIFICATION OF REFERRAL

FC 13
Notification of referral to the *tribunal*

IF THE TRIBUNAL IS ARBITRATION

W1.4(5)
If the *tribunal* is arbitration, the arbitration procedure, the place where the arbitration is to be held and the method of choosing the arbitrator are those stated in the CD

TRIBUNAL'S POWERS

W1.4(4)
The *tribunal* has the powers to reconsider any decision of the *Adjudicator* and review and revise any action or inaction of the *SM* related to the dispute

ADMISSIBLE EVIDENCE

W1.4(4)
A Party is not limited in the *tribunal* proceedings to the information, evidence or arguments put to the *Adjudicator*

ADJUDICATOR NOT CALLED AS WITNESS

W1.4(6)
A Party does not call the *Adjudicator* as a witness in *tribunal* proceedings

TRIBUNAL DECIDES

W1.4(4)
The *tribunal* settles the dispute referred to it

Flow chart W1 Sheet 5 of 5
Dispute resolution procedure W1

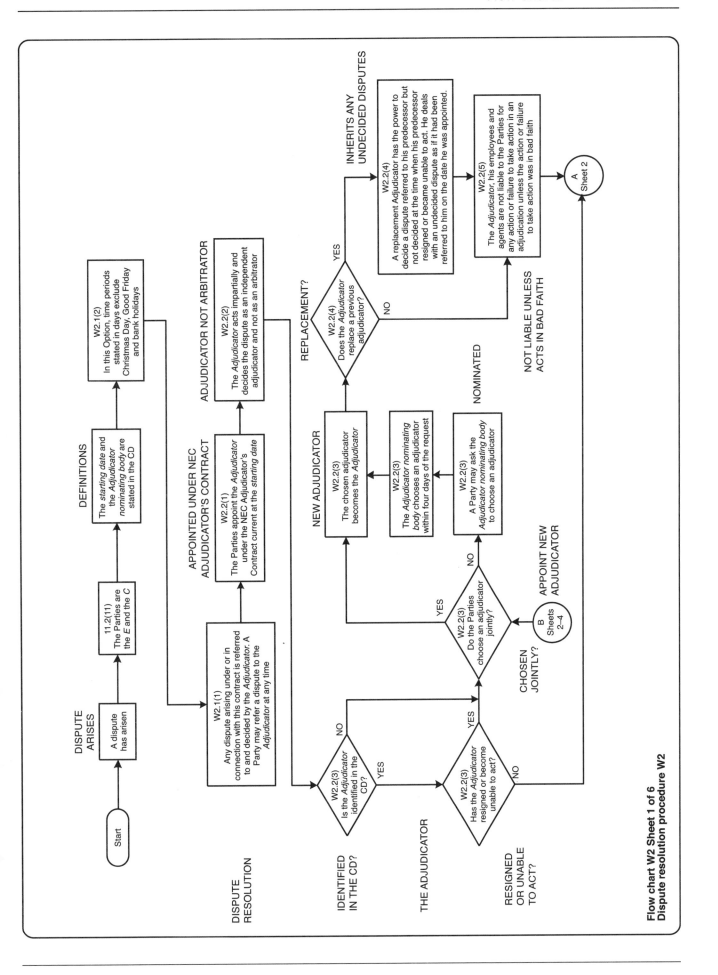

Flow chart W2 Sheet 1 of 6
Dispute resolution procedure W2

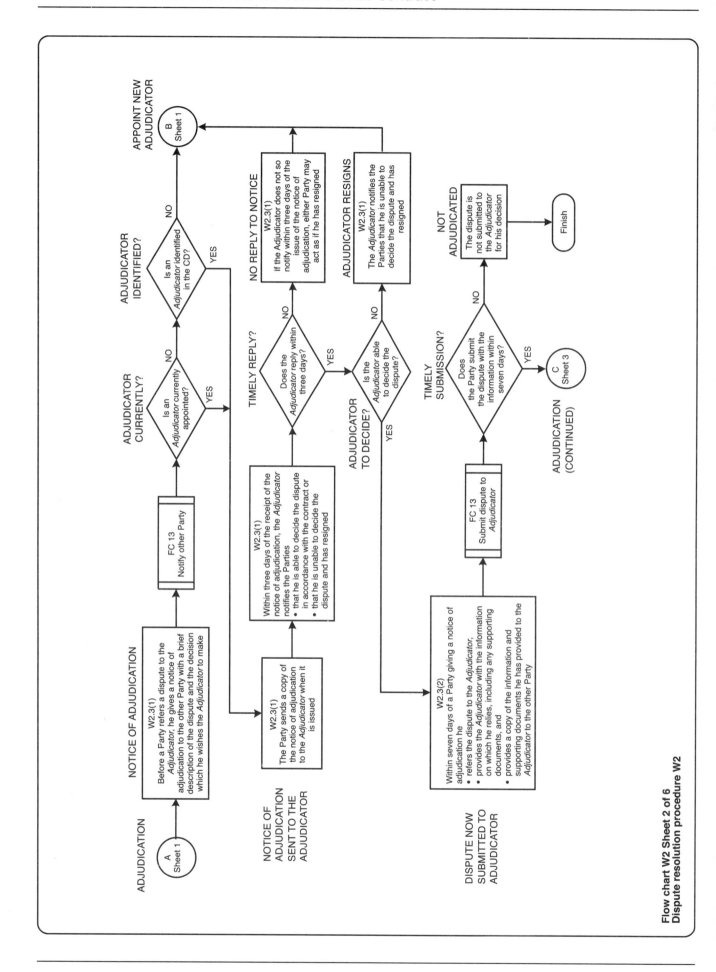

ADJUDICATION

A Sheet 1

NOTICE OF ADJUDICATION

W2.3(1)
Before a Party refers a dispute to the *Adjudicator*, he gives a notice of adjudication to the other Party with a brief description of the dispute and the decision which he wishes the *Adjudicator* to make

FC 13
Notify other Party

ADJUDICATOR CURRENTLY?

Is an *Adjudicator* currently appointed?

NO

YES

ADJUDICATOR IDENTIFIED?

Is an *Adjudicator* identified in the CD?

NO

YES

APPOINT NEW ADJUDICATOR

B Sheet 1

NOTICE OF ADJUDICATION SENT TO THE ADJUDICATOR

W2.3(1)
The Party sends a copy of the notice of adjudication to the *Adjudicator* when it is issued

W2.3(1)
Within three days of the receipt of the notice of adjudication, the *Adjudicator* notifies the Parties
• that he is able to decide the dispute in accordance with the contract or
• that he is unable to decide the dispute and has resigned

TIMELY REPLY?

Does the *Adjudicator* reply within three days?

NO

YES

NO REPLY TO NOTICE

W2.3(1)
If the *Adjudicator* does not so notify within three days of the issue of the notice of adjudication, either Party may act as if he has resigned

ADJUDICATOR TO DECIDE?

Is the *Adjudicator* able to decide the dispute?

NO

YES

ADJUDICATOR RESIGNS

W2.3(1)
The *Adjudicator* notifies the Parties that he is unable to decide the dispute and has resigned

DISPUTE NOW SUBMITTED TO ADJUDICATOR

W2.3(2)
Within seven days of a Party giving a notice of adjudication he
• refers the dispute to the *Adjudicator*,
• provides the *Adjudicator* with the information on which he relies, including any supporting documents, and
• provides a copy of the information and supporting documents he has provided to the *Adjudicator* to the other Party

FC 13
Submit dispute to *Adjudicator*

TIMELY SUBMISSION?

Does the Party submit the dispute with the information within seven days?

NO

YES

NOT ADJUDICATED

The dispute is not submitted to the *Adjudicator* for his decision

Finish

ADJUDICATION (CONTINUED)

C Sheet 3

Flow chart W2 Sheet 2 of 6
Dispute resolution procedure W2

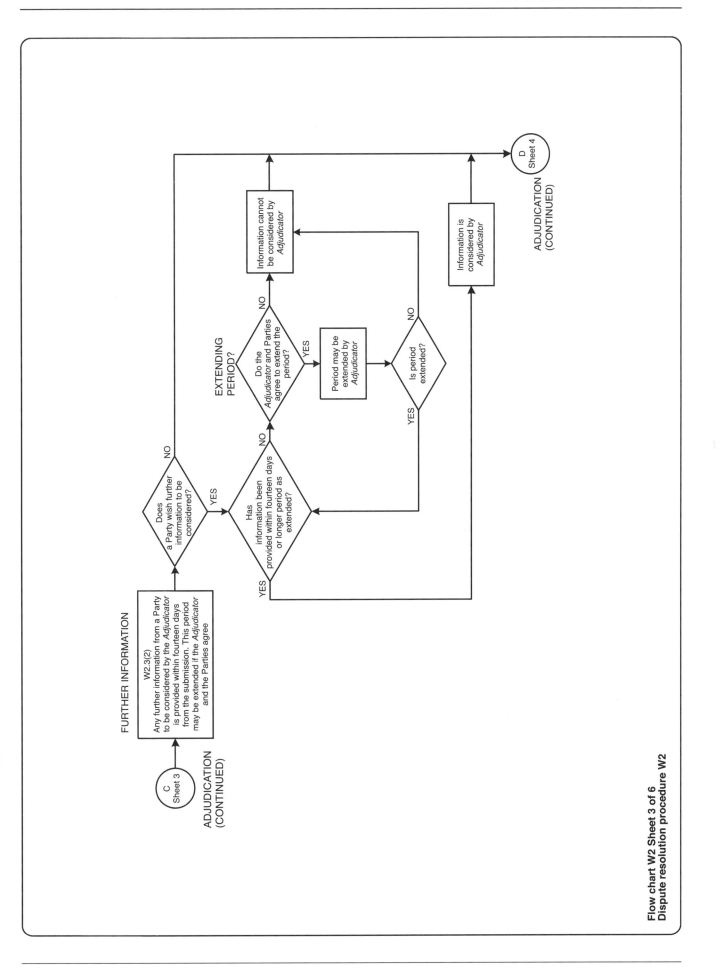

FURTHER INFORMATION

W2.3(2)
Any further information from a Party to be considered by the *Adjudicator* is provided within fourteen days from the submission. This period may be extended if the *Adjudicator* and the Parties agree

C
Sheet 3

ADJUDICATION
(CONTINUED)

Does a Party wish further information to be considered?

NO

YES

Has information been provided within fourteen days or longer period as extended?

YES

NO

EXTENDING PERIOD?

Do the *Adjudicator* and Parties agree to extend the period?

NO

YES

Information cannot be considered by *Adjudicator*

Period may be extended by *Adjudicator*

Is period extended?

NO

YES

Information is considered by *Adjudicator*

D
Sheet 4

ADJUDICATION
(CONTINUED)

**Flow chart W2 Sheet 3 of 6
Dispute resolution procedure W2**

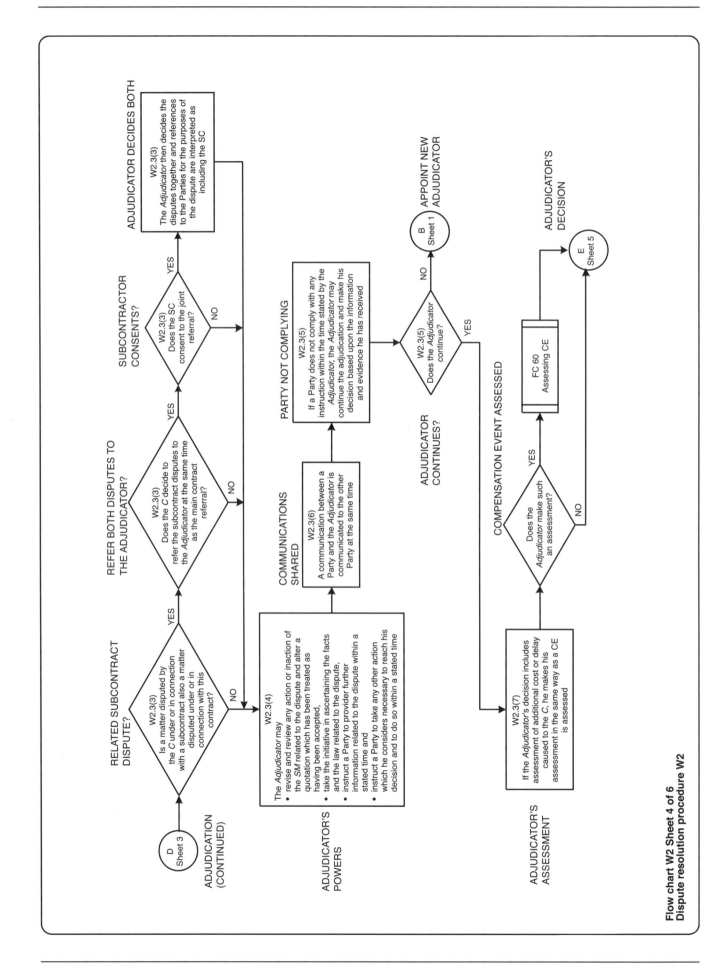

Flow chart W2 Sheet 4 of 6
Dispute resolution procedure W2

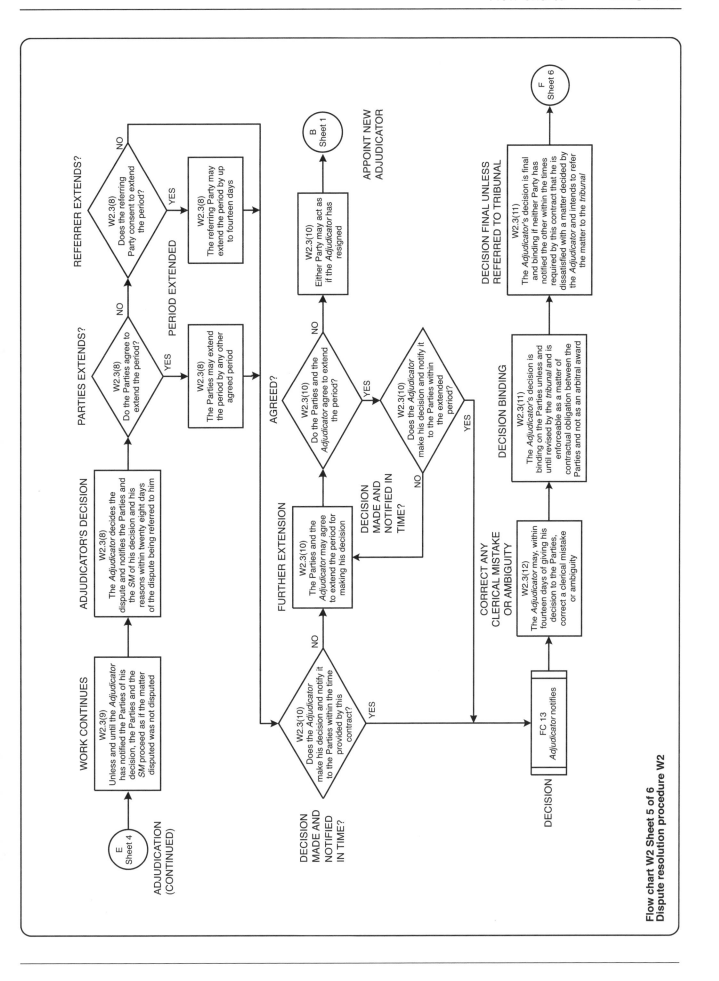

Flow chart W2 Sheet 5 of 6
Dispute resolution procedure W2

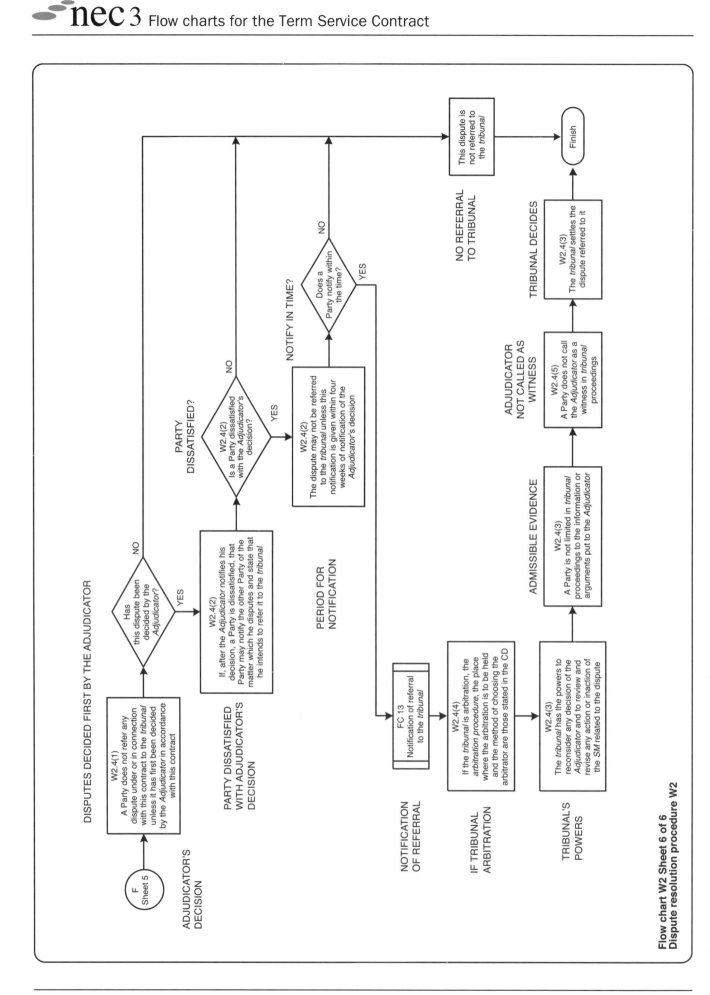

DISPUTES DECIDED FIRST BY THE ADJUDICATOR

ADJUDICATOR'S DECISION

F Sheet 5

W2.4(1)
A Party does not refer any dispute under or in connection with this contract to the *tribunal* unless it has first been decided by the *Adjudicator* in accordance with this contract

PARTY DISSATISFIED WITH ADJUDICATOR'S DECISION

W2.4(2)
If, after the *Adjudicator* notifies his decision, a Party is dissatisfied, that Party may notify the other Party of the matter which he disputes and state that he intends to refer it to the *tribunal*

Has this dispute been decided by the *Adjudicator*? — NO / YES

PARTY DISSATISFIED?

W2.4(2)
Is a Party dissatisfied with the *Adjudicator's* decision? — NO / YES

PERIOD FOR NOTIFICATION

W2.4(2)
The dispute may not be referred to the *tribunal* unless this notification is given within four weeks of notification of *Adjudicator's* decision

NOTIFY IN TIME?

Does a Party notify within the time? — NO / YES

This dispute is not referred to the *tribunal*

NO REFERRAL TO TRIBUNAL

Finish

NOTIFICATION OF REFERRAL

FC 13
Notification of referral to the *tribunal*

IF TRIBUNAL ARBITRATION

W2.4(4)
If the *tribunal* is arbitration, the *arbitration procedure*, the place where the arbitration is to be held and the method of choosing the arbitrator are those stated in the CD

TRIBUNAL'S POWERS

W2.4(3)
The *tribunal* has the powers to reconsider any decision of the *Adjudicator* and to review and revise any action or inaction of the *SM* related to the dispute

ADMISSIBLE EVIDENCE

W2.4(3)
A Party is not limited in *tribunal* proceedings to the information or arguments put to the *Adjudicator*

ADJUDICATOR NOT CALLED AS WITNESS

W2.4(5)
A Party does not call the *Adjudicator* as a witness in *tribunal* proceedings

TRIBUNAL DECIDES

W2.4(3)
The *tribunal* settles the dispute referred to it

**Flow chart W2 Sheet 6 of 6
Dispute resolution procedure W2**

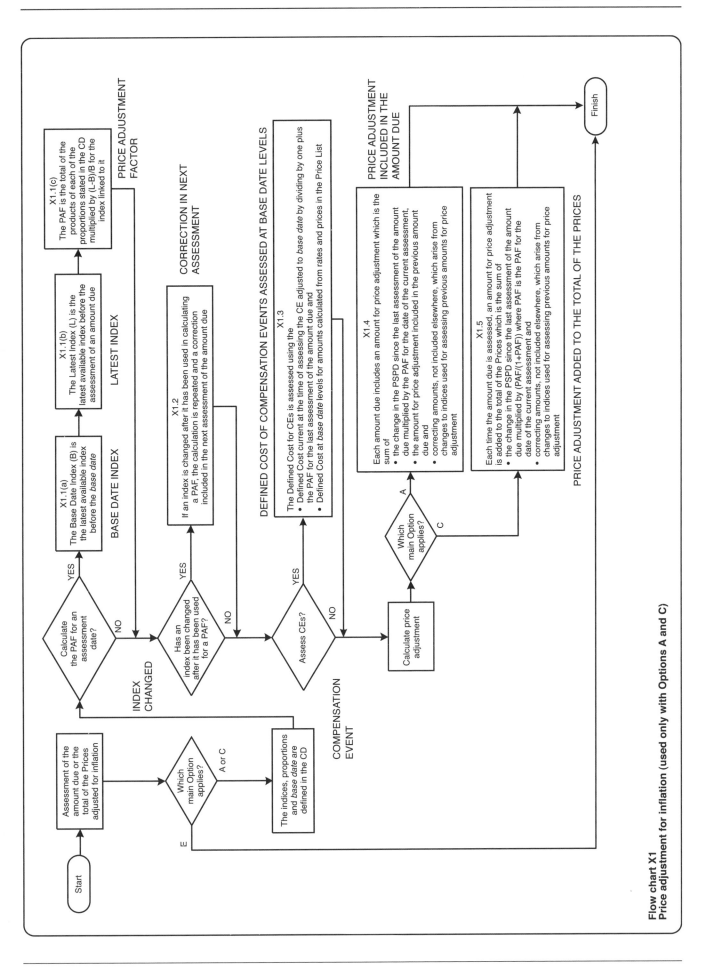

Flow chart X1
Price adjustment for inflation (used only with Options A and C)

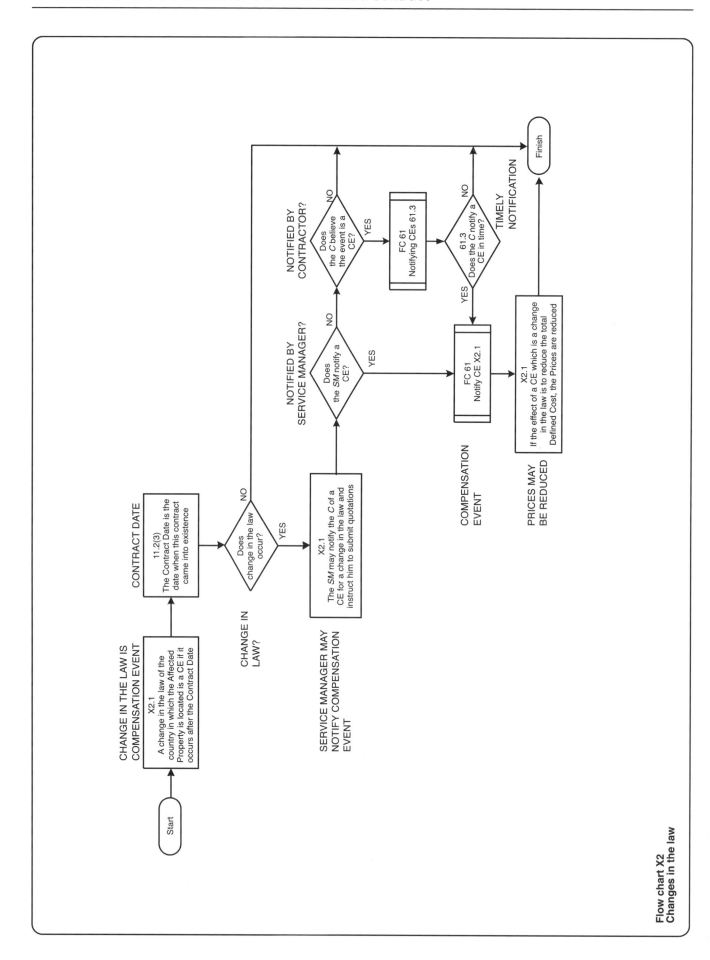

Flow chart X2
Changes in the law

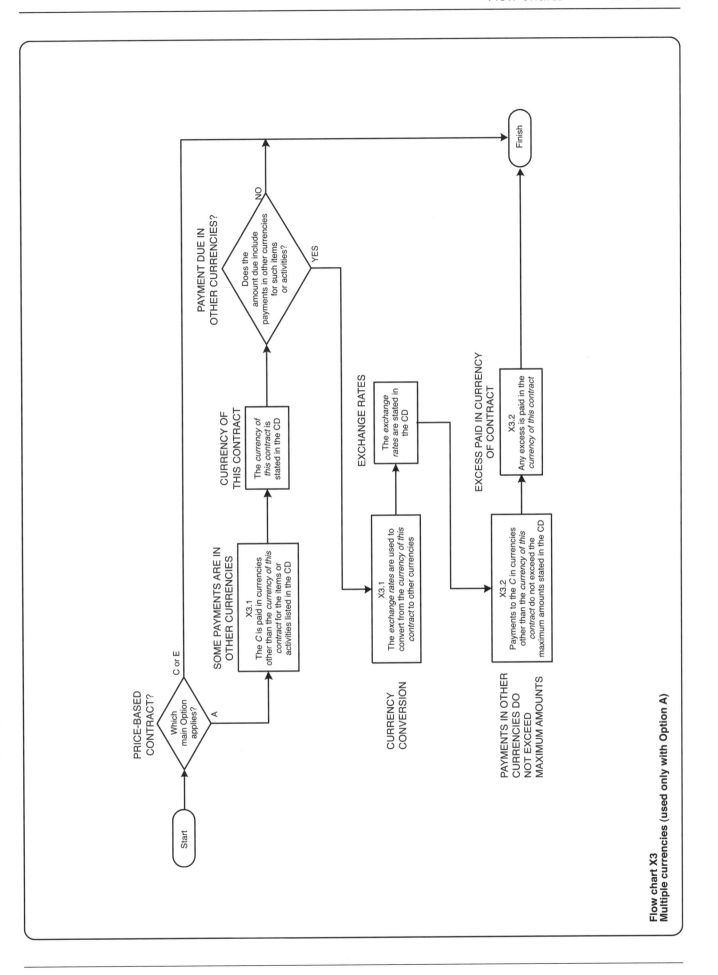

Flow chart X3
Multiple currencies (used only with Option A)

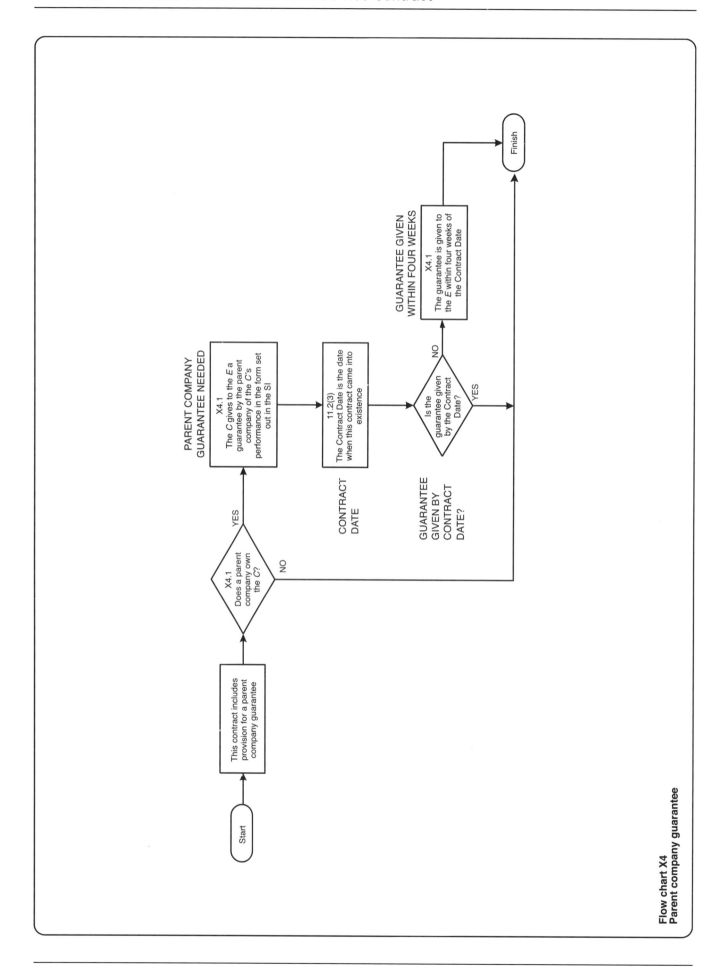

Flow chart X4
Parent company guarantee

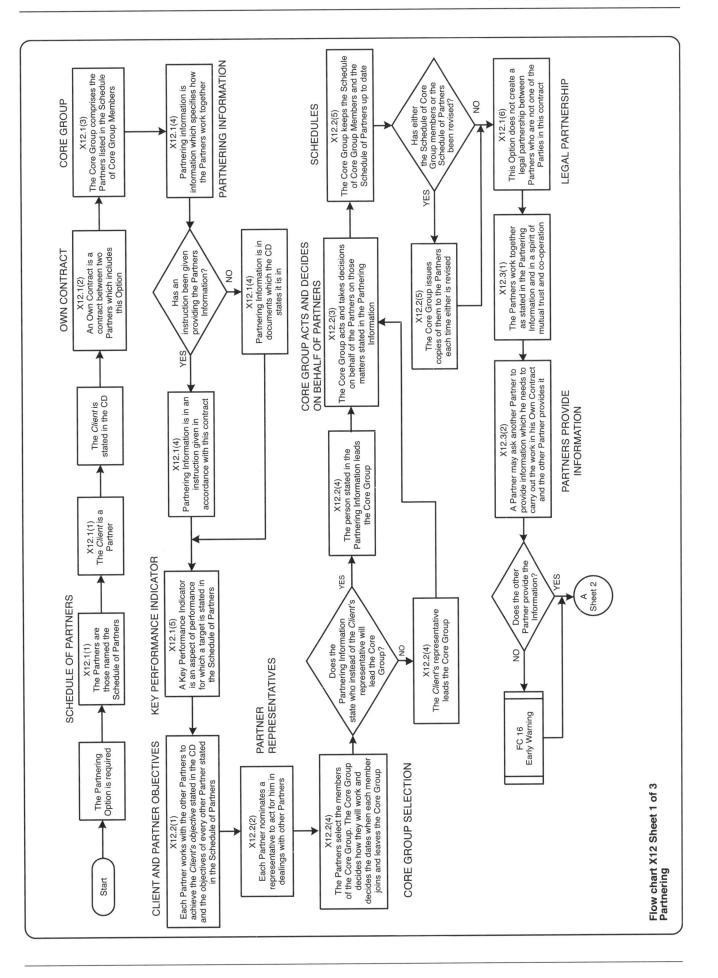

**Flow chart X12 Sheet 1 of 3
Partnering**

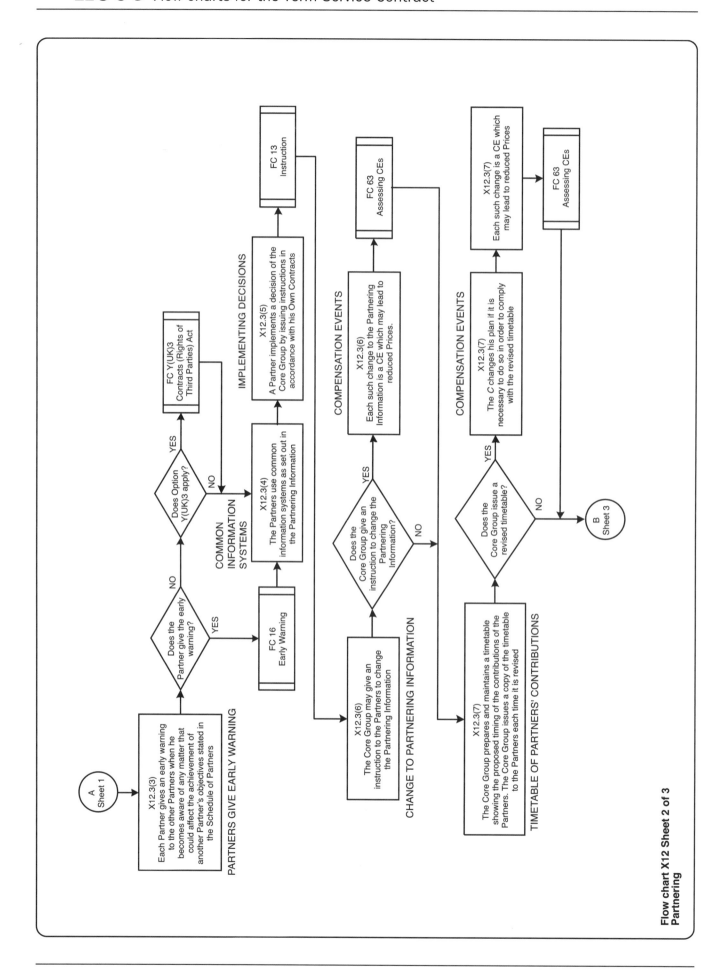

A
Sheet 1

X12.3(3)
Each Partner gives an early warning to the other Partners when he becomes aware of any matter that could affect the achievement of another Partner's objectives stated in the Schedule of Partners

PARTNERS GIVE EARLY WARNING

Does the Partner give the early warning?

YES → FC 16 Early Warning

NO → Does Option Y(UK)3 apply?

YES → FC Y(UK)3 Contracts (Rights of Third Parties) Act

NO →

X12.3(4)
The Partners use common information systems as set out in the Partnering Information

COMMON INFORMATION SYSTEMS

X12.3(5)
A Partner implements a decision of the Core Group by issuing instructions in accordance with his Own Contracts

IMPLEMENTING DECISIONS

→ FC 13 Instruction

X12.3(6)
The Core Group may give an instruction to the Partners to change the Partnering Information

CHANGE TO PARTNERING INFORMATION

Does the Core Group give an instruction to change the Partnering Information?

YES → X12.3(6)
Each such change to the Partnering Information is a CE which may lead to reduced Prices.

COMPENSATION EVENTS

→ FC 63 Assessing CEs

NO →

X12.3(7)
The Core Group prepares and maintains a timetable showing the proposed timing of the contributions of the Partners. The Core Group issues a copy of the timetable to the Partners each time it is revised

TIMETABLE OF PARTNERS' CONTRIBUTIONS

Does the Core Group issue a revised timetable?

YES → X12.3(7)
The C changes his plan if it is necessary to do so in order to comply with the revised timetable

COMPENSATION EVENTS

→ X12.3(7)
Each such change is a CE which may lead to reduced Prices

→ FC 63 Assessing CEs

NO →

B
Sheet 3

Flow chart X12 Sheet 2 of 3
Partnering

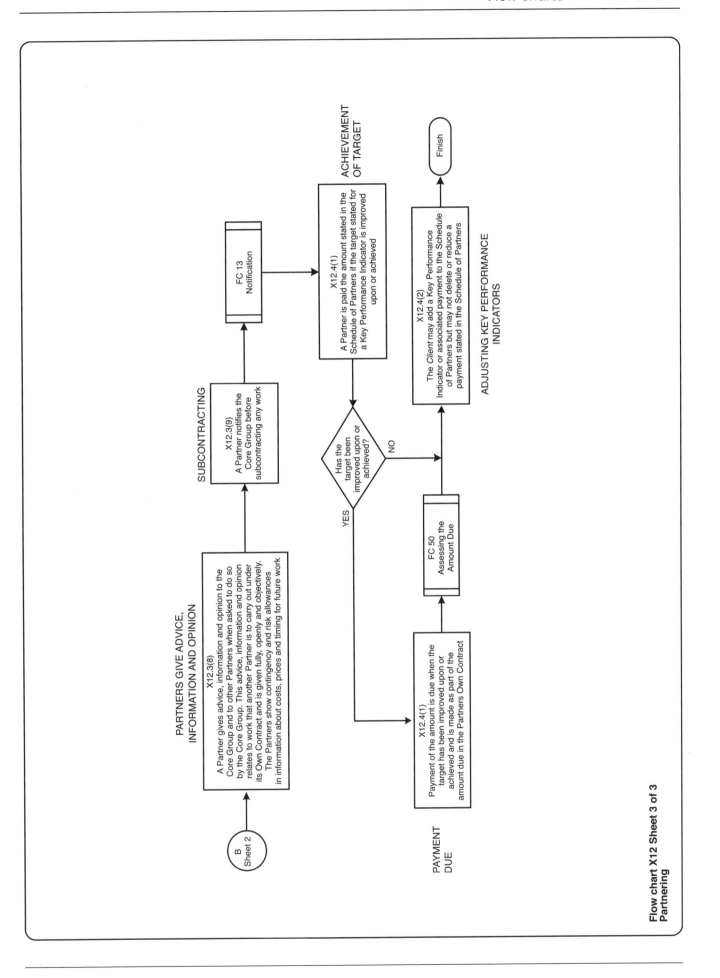

PARTNERS GIVE ADVICE,
INFORMATION AND OPINION

X12.3(8)

A Partner gives advice, information and opinion to the
Core Group and to other Partners when asked to do so
by the Core Group. This advice, information and opinion
relates to work that another Partner is to carry out under
its Own Contract and is given fully, openly and objectively.
The Partners show contingency and risk allowances
in information about costs, prices and timing for future work

SUBCONTRACTING

X12.3(9)

A Partner notifies the
Core Group before
subcontracting any work

FC 13

Notification

ACHIEVEMENT
OF TARGET

X12.4(1)

A Partner is paid the amount stated in the
Schedule of Partners if the target stated for
a Key Performance Indicator is improved
upon or achieved

Has the
target been
improved upon or
achieved?

YES

NO

PAYMENT
DUE

X12.4(1)

Payment of the amount is due when the
target has been improved upon or
achieved and is made as part of the
amount due in the Partners Own Contract

FC 50

Assessing the
Amount Due

X12.4(2)

The *Client* may add a Key Performance
Indicator or associated payment to the Schedule
of Partners but may not delete or reduce a
payment stated in the Schedule of Partners

ADJUSTING KEY PERFORMANCE
INDICATORS

Finish

B
Sheet 2

Flow chart X12 Sheet 3 of 3
Partnering

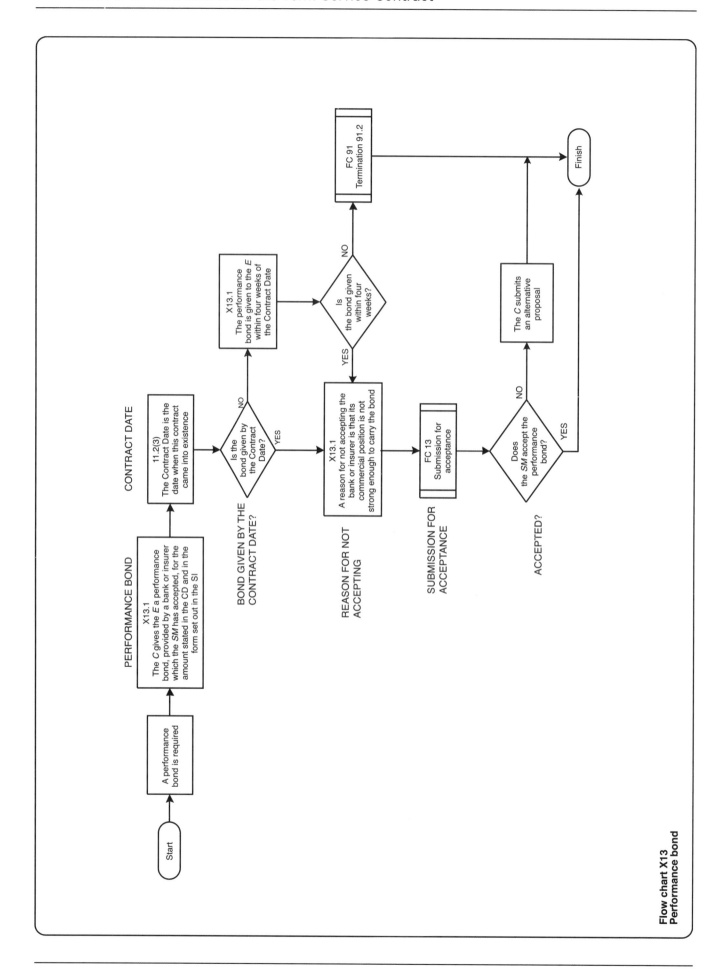

PERFORMANCE BOND

X13.1
The *C* gives the *E* a performance bond, provided by a bank or insurer which the *SM* has accepted, for the amount stated in the CD and in the form set out in the SI

CONTRACT DATE

11.2(3)
The Contract Date is the date when this contract came into existence

BOND GIVEN BY THE CONTRACT DATE?

Is the bond given by the Contract Date?

X13.1
The performance bond is given to the *E* within four weeks of the Contract Date

Is the bond given within four weeks?

REASON FOR NOT ACCEPTING

X13.1
A reason for not accepting the bank or insurer is that its commercial position is not strong enough to carry the bond

SUBMISSION FOR ACCEPTANCE

FC 13
Submission for acceptance

ACCEPTED?

Does the *SM* accept the performance bond?

The *C* submits an alternative proposal

FC 91
Termination 91.2

Start

A performance bond is required

Finish

NO / YES

Flow chart X13
Performance bond

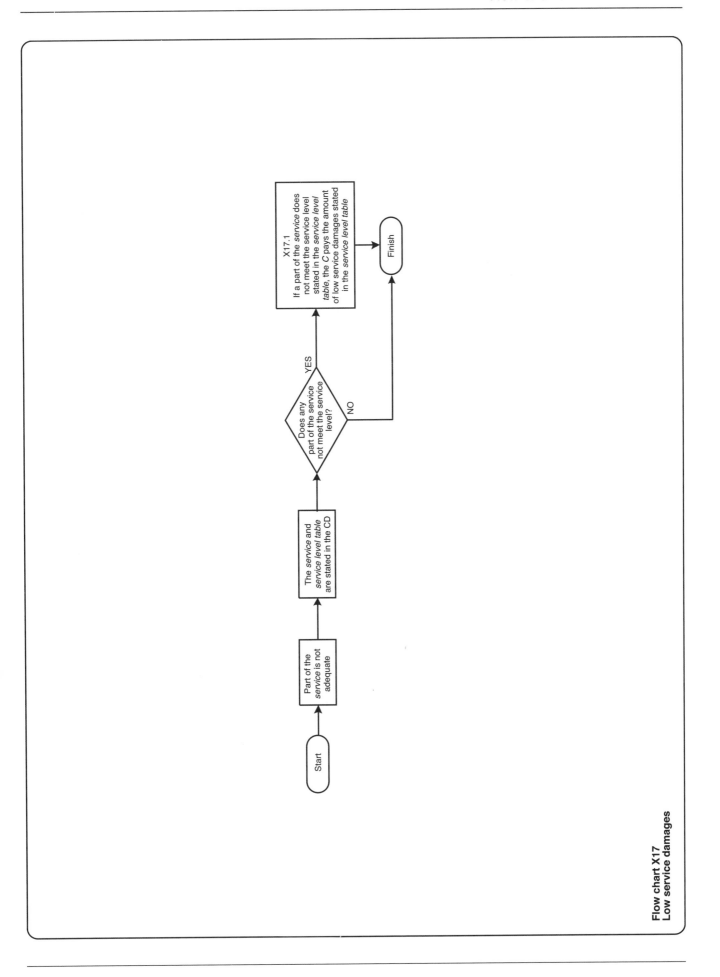

Start → Part of the *service* is not adequate → The *service* and *service level table* are stated in the CD → Does any part of the *service* not meet the *service level?*

YES → X17.1
If a part of the *service* does not meet the *service level* stated in the *service level table*, the *C* pays the amount of low service damages stated in the *service level table* → **Finish**

NO → **Finish**

Flow chart X17
Low service damages

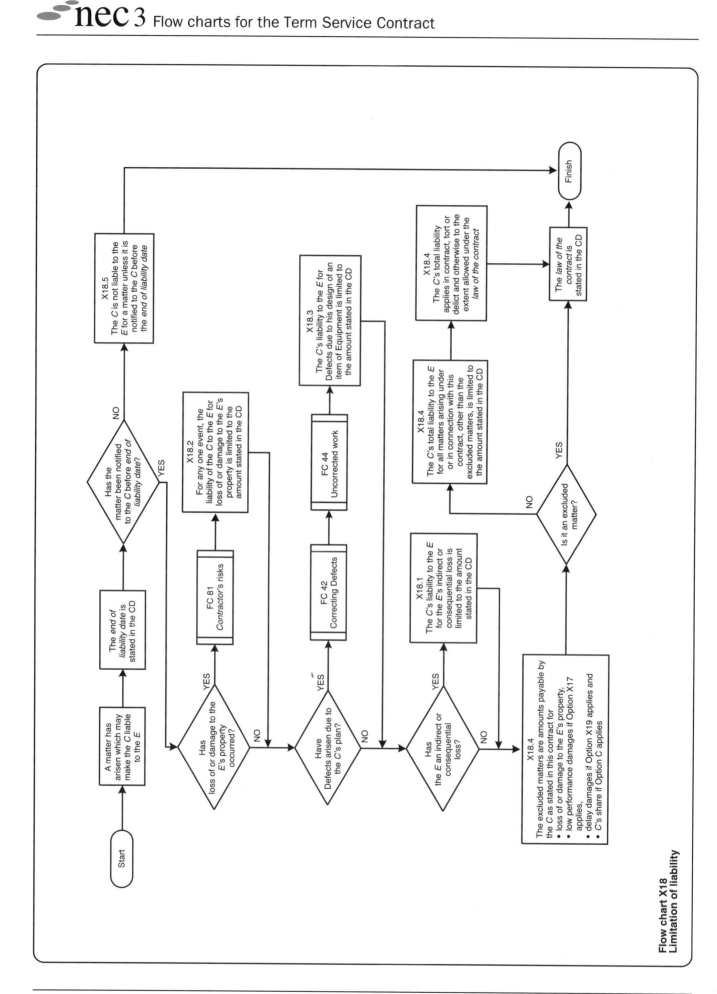

Flow chart X18
Limitation of liability

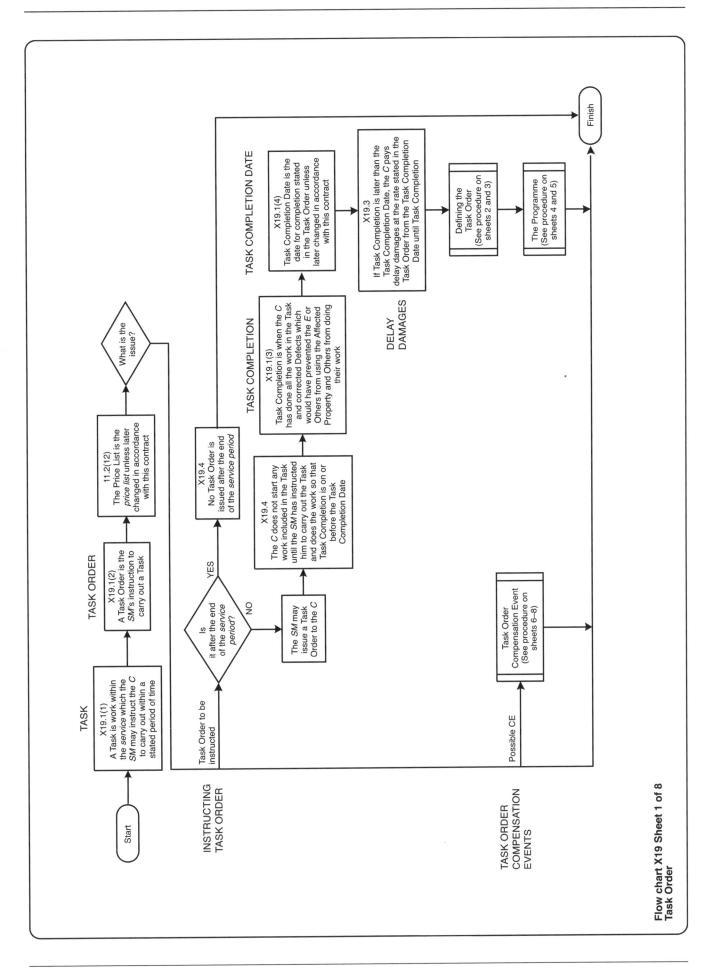

Flow chart X19 Sheet 1 of 8
Task Order

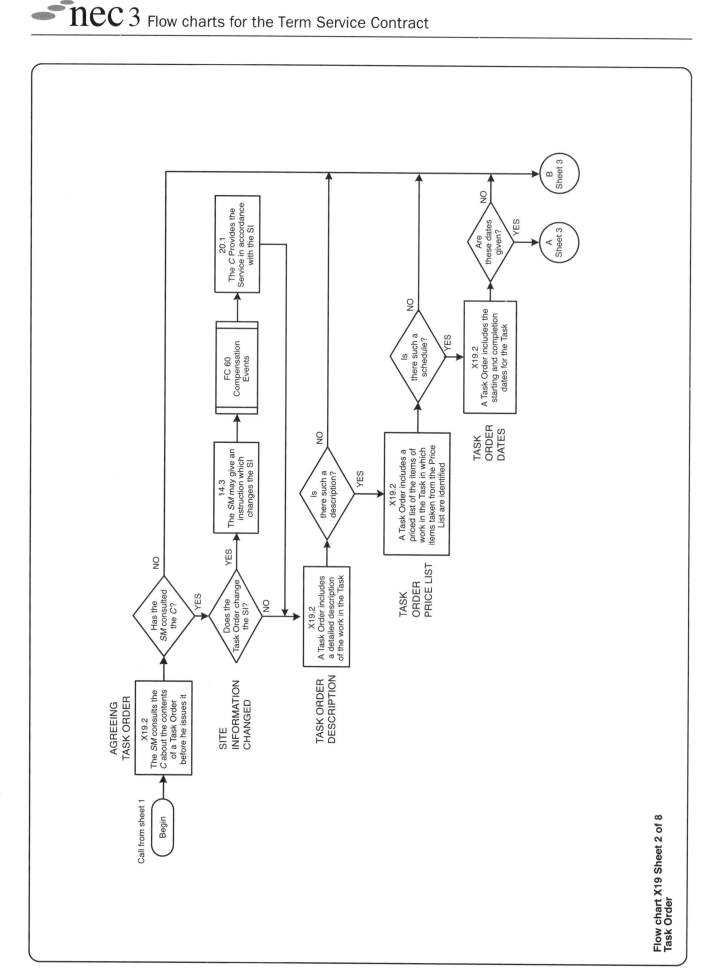

Flow chart X19 Sheet 2 of 8
Task Order

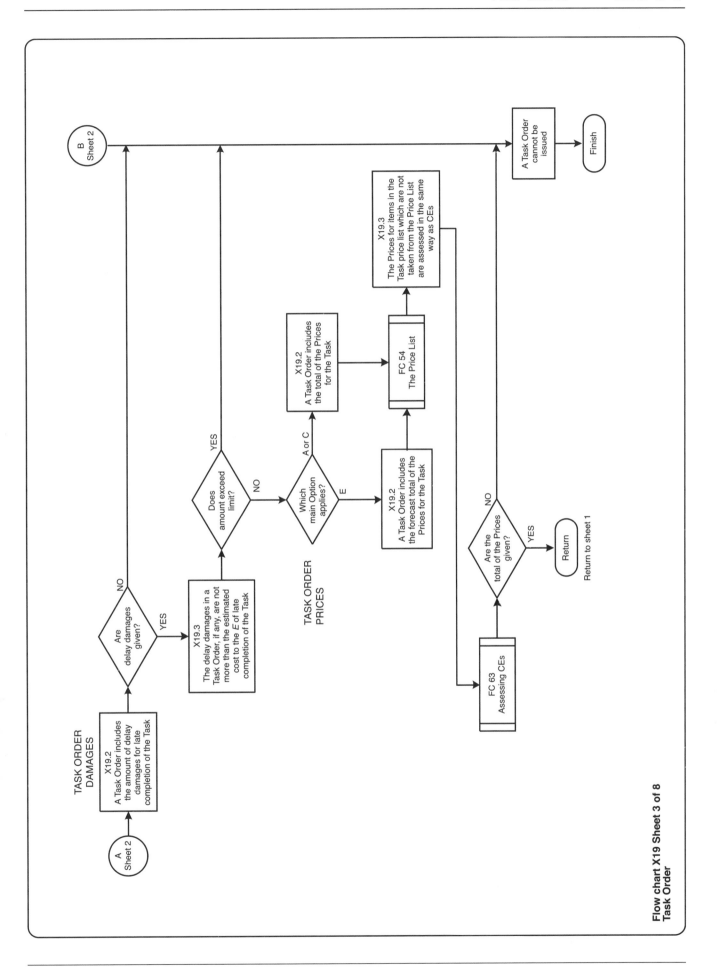

Flow chart X19 Sheet 3 of 8
Task Order

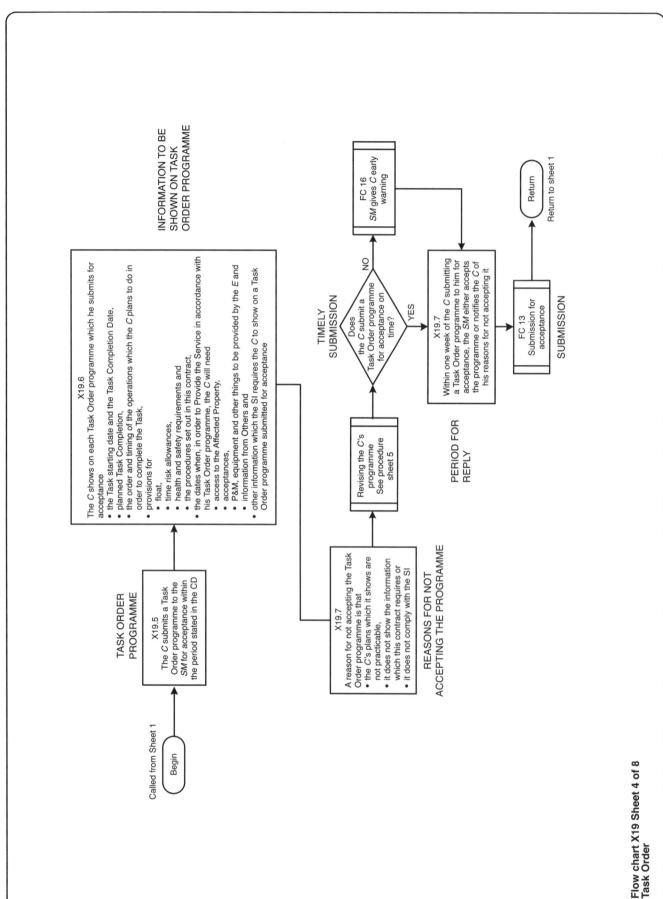

INFORMATION TO BE SHOWN ON TASK ORDER PROGRAMME

X19.6

The C shows on each Task Order programme which he submits for acceptance
- the Task starting date and the Task Completion Date,
- planned Task Completion,
- the order and timing of the operations which the C plans to do in order to complete the Task,
- provisions for
  - float,
  - time risk allowances,
  - health and safety requirements and
  - the procedures set out in this contract,
- the dates when, in order to Provide the Service in accordance with his Task Order programme, the C will need
  - access to the Affected Property,
  - acceptances,
  - P&M, equipment and other things to be provided by the E and
  - information from Others and
- other information which the SI requires the C to show on a Task Order programme submitted for acceptance

TASK ORDER PROGRAMME

X19.5
The C submits a Task Order programme to the SM for acceptance within the period stated in the CD

Called from Sheet 1

(Begin)

TIMELY SUBMISSION

Does the C submit a Task Order programme for acceptance on time?

NO → FC 16 — SM gives C early warning

YES ↓

PERIOD FOR REPLY

X19.7
Within one week of the C submitting a Task Order programme to him for acceptance, the SM either accepts the programme or notifies the C of his reasons for not accepting it

SUBMISSION

FC 13 — Submission for acceptance

(Return)

Return to sheet 1

Revising the C's programme
See procedure sheet 5

X19.7
A reason for not accepting the Task Order programme is that
- the C's plans which it shows are not practicable,
- it does not show the information which this contract requires or
- it does not comply with the SI

REASONS FOR NOT ACCEPTING THE PROGRAMME

Flow chart X19 Sheet 4 of 8
Task Order

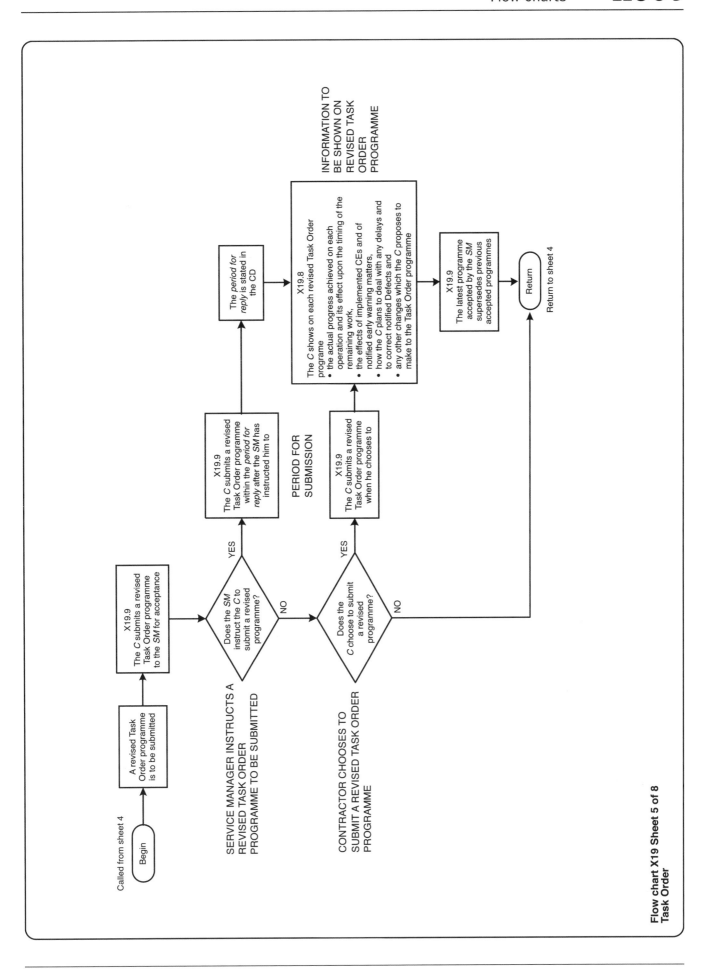

Called from sheet 4

Begin

A revised Task Order programme is to be submitted

X19.9
The *C* submits a revised Task Order programme to the *SM* for acceptance

SERVICE MANAGER INSTRUCTS A REVISED TASK ORDER PROGRAMME TO BE SUBMITTED

Does the *SM* instruct the *C* to submit a revised programme?

YES →

NO ↓

X19.9
The *C* submits a revised Task Order programme within the *period for reply* after the *SM* has instructed him to

PERIOD FOR SUBMISSION

CONTRACTOR CHOOSES TO SUBMIT A REVISED TASK ORDER PROGRAMME

Does the *C* choose to submit a revised programme?

YES →

NO →

X19.9
The *C* submits a revised Task Order programme when he chooses to

The *period for reply* is stated in the CD

X19.8
The *C* shows on each revised Task Order programe
• the actual progress achieved on each operation and its effect upon the timing of the remaining work,
• the effects of implemented CEs and of notified early warning matters,
• how the *C* plans to deal with any delays and to correct notified Defects and
• any other changes which the *C* proposes to make to the Task Order programme

INFORMATION TO BE SHOWN ON REVISED TASK ORDER PROGRAMME

X19.9
The latest programme accepted by the *SM* supersedes previous accepted programmes

Return

Return to sheet 4

Flow chart X19 Sheet 5 of 8
Task Order

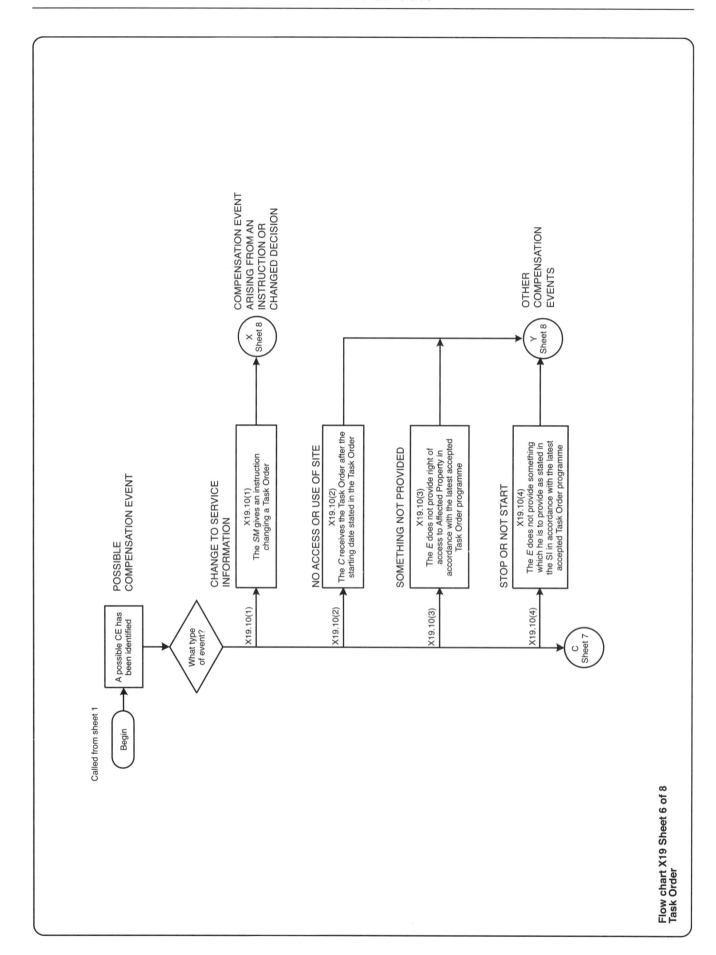

Called from sheet 1

Begin

A possible CE has been identified

POSSIBLE COMPENSATION EVENT

What type of event?

X19.10(1)

CHANGE TO SERVICE INFORMATION

X19.10(1)
The *SM* gives an instruction changing a Task Order

COMPENSATION EVENT ARISING FROM AN INSTRUCTION OR CHANGED DECISION

X
Sheet 8

X19.10(2)

NO ACCESS OR USE OF SITE

X19.10(2)
The *C* receives the Task Order after the starting date stated in the Task Order

X19.10(3)

SOMETHING NOT PROVIDED

X19.10(3)
The *E* does not provide right of access to Affected Property in accordance with the latest accepted Task Order programme

X19.10(4)

STOP OR NOT START

X19.10(4)
The *E* does not provide something which he is to provide as stated in the SI in accordance with the latest accepted Task Order programme

OTHER COMPENSATION EVENTS

Y
Sheet 8

C
Sheet 7

Flow chart X19 Sheet 6 of 8
Task Order

www.neccontract.com

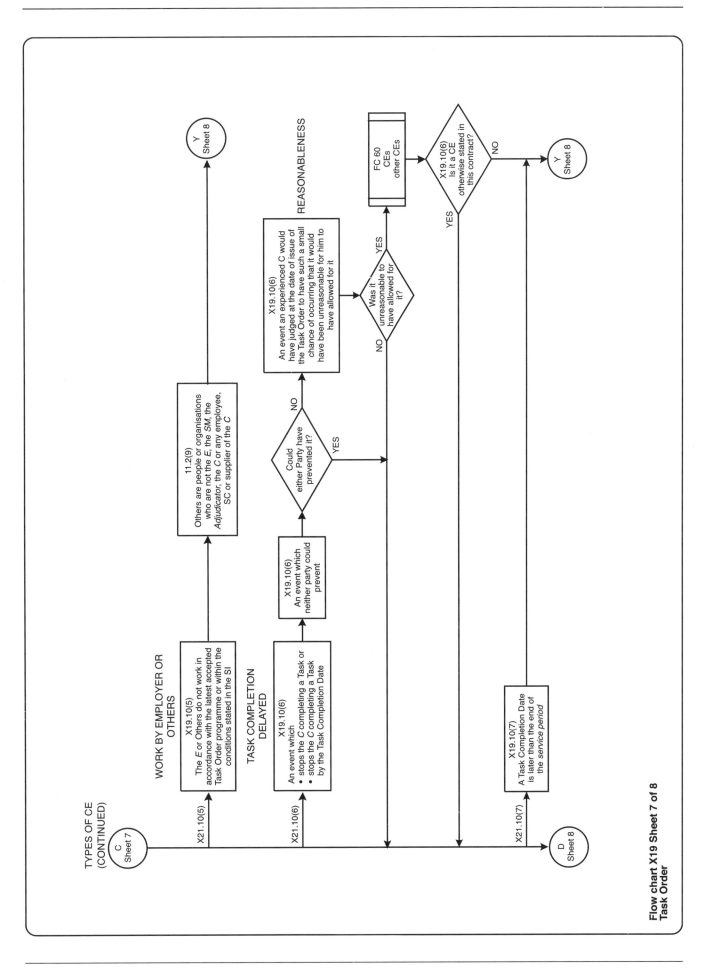

TYPES OF CE (CONTINUED)

C Sheet 7

WORK BY EMPLOYER OR OTHERS

X21.10(5)

X19.10(5)
The *E* or Others do not work in accordance with the latest accepted Task Order programme or within the conditions stated in the SI

11.2(9)
Others are people or organisations who are not the *E*, the *SM*, the *Adjudicator*, the *C* or any employee, SC or supplier of the *C*

Y Sheet 8

TASK COMPLETION DELAYED

X21.10(6)

X19.10(6)
An event which
• stops the *C* completing a Task or
• stops the *C* completing a Task by the Task Completion Date

X19.10(6)
An event which neither party could prevent

Could either Party have prevented it?

YES

NO

X19.10(6)
An event an experienced *C* would have judged at the date of issue of the Task Order to have such a small chance of occurring that it would have been unreasonable for him to have allowed for it

REASONABLENESS

Was it unreasonable to have allowed for it?

NO

YES

FC 60
CEs
other CEs

X19.10(6)
Is it a CE otherwise stated in this contract?

YES

NO

Y Sheet 8

X21.10(7)

X19.10(7)
A Task Completion Date is later than the end of the *service period*

D Sheet 8

**Flow chart X19 Sheet 7 of 8
Task Order**

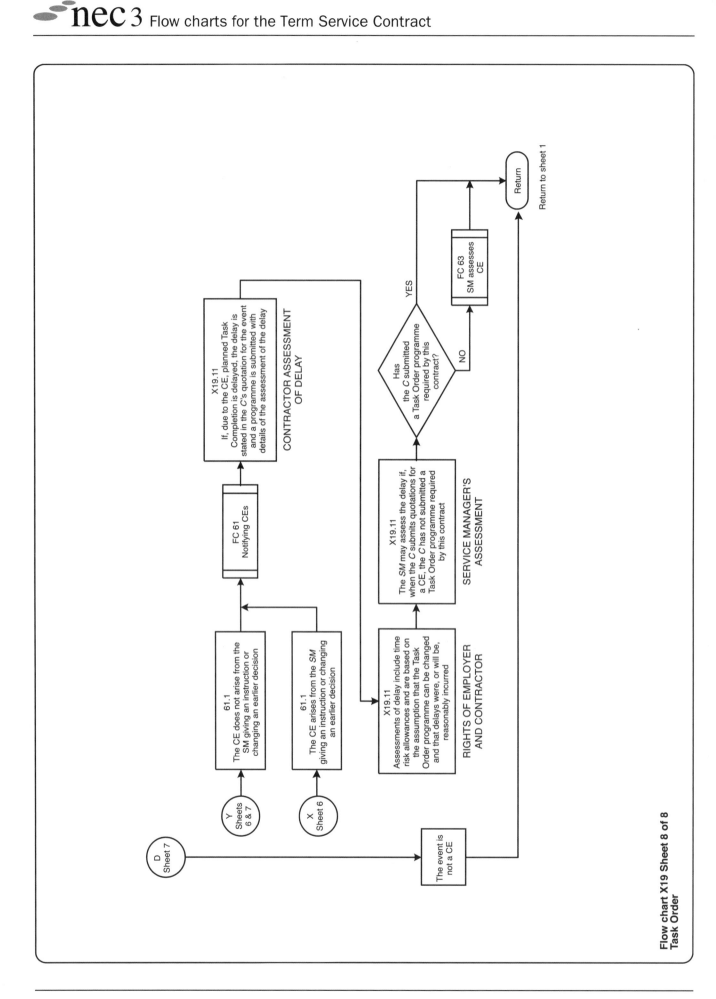

Flow chart X19 Sheet 8 of 8
Task Order

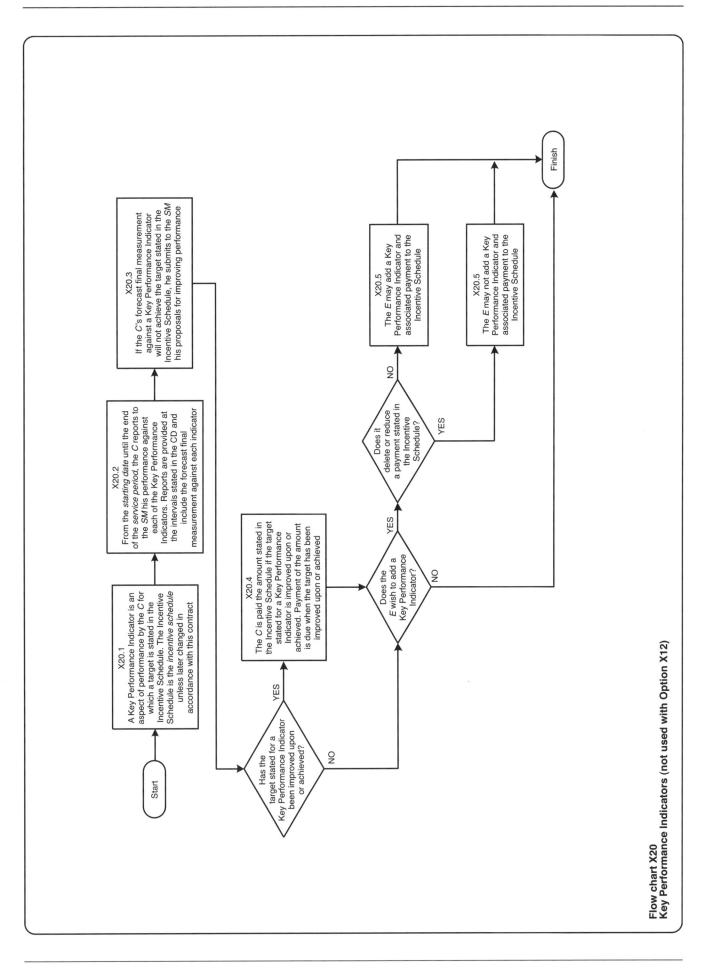

Flow chart X20
Key Performance Indicators (not used with Option X12)

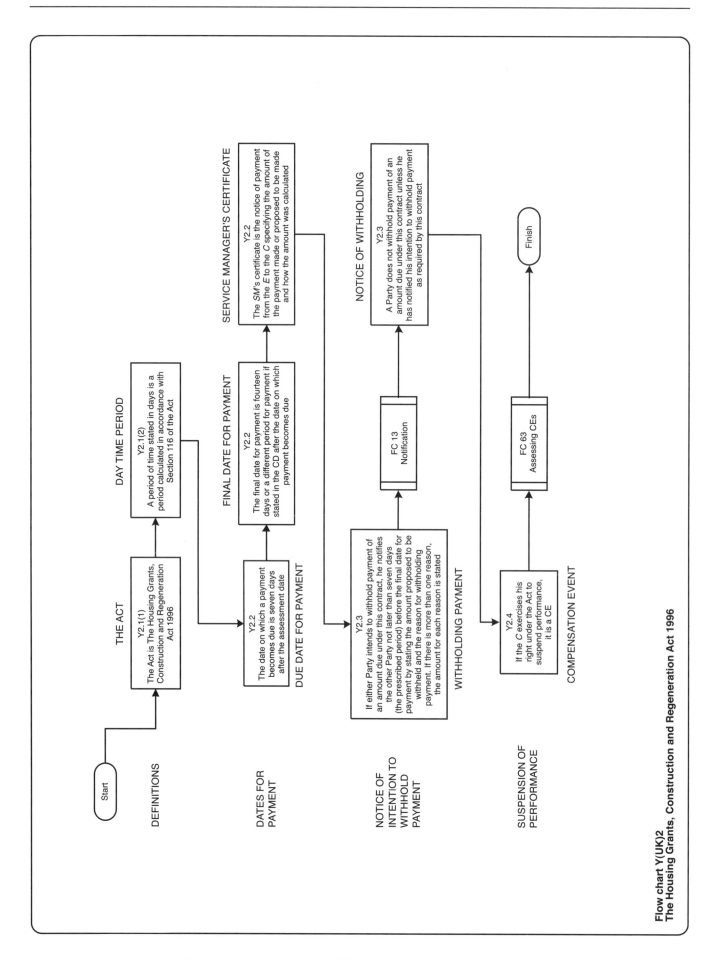

DEFINITIONS

THE ACT

Y2.1(1)

The Act is The Housing Grants, Construction and Regeneration Act 1996

DAY TIME PERIOD

Y2.1(2)

A period of time stated in days is a period calculated in accordance with Section 116 of the Act

SERVICE MANAGER'S CERTIFICATE

Y2.2

The *SM's* certificate is the notice of payment from the *E* to the *C* specifying the amount of the payment made or proposed to be made and how the amount was calculated

DATES FOR PAYMENT

DUE DATE FOR PAYMENT

Y2.2

The date on which a payment becomes due is seven days after the assessment date

FINAL DATE FOR PAYMENT

Y2.2

The final date for payment is fourteen days or a different period for payment if stated in the CD after the date on which payment becomes due

NOTICE OF INTENTION TO WITHHOLD PAYMENT

Y2.3

If either Party intends to withhold payment of an amount due under this contract, he notifies the other Party not later than seven days (the prescribed period) before the final date for payment by stating the amount proposed to be withheld and the reason for withholding payment. If there is more than one reason, the amount for each reason is stated

WITHHOLDING PAYMENT

FC 13
Notification

NOTICE OF WITHHOLDING

Y2.3

A Party does not withhold payment of an amount due under this contract unless he has notified his intention to withhold payment as required by this contract

SUSPENSION OF PERFORMANCE

Y2.4

If the *C* exercises his right under the Act to suspend performance, it is a CE

COMPENSATION EVENT

FC 63
Assessing CEs

Start

Finish

Flow chart Y(UK)2
The Housing Grants, Construction and Regeneration Act 1996

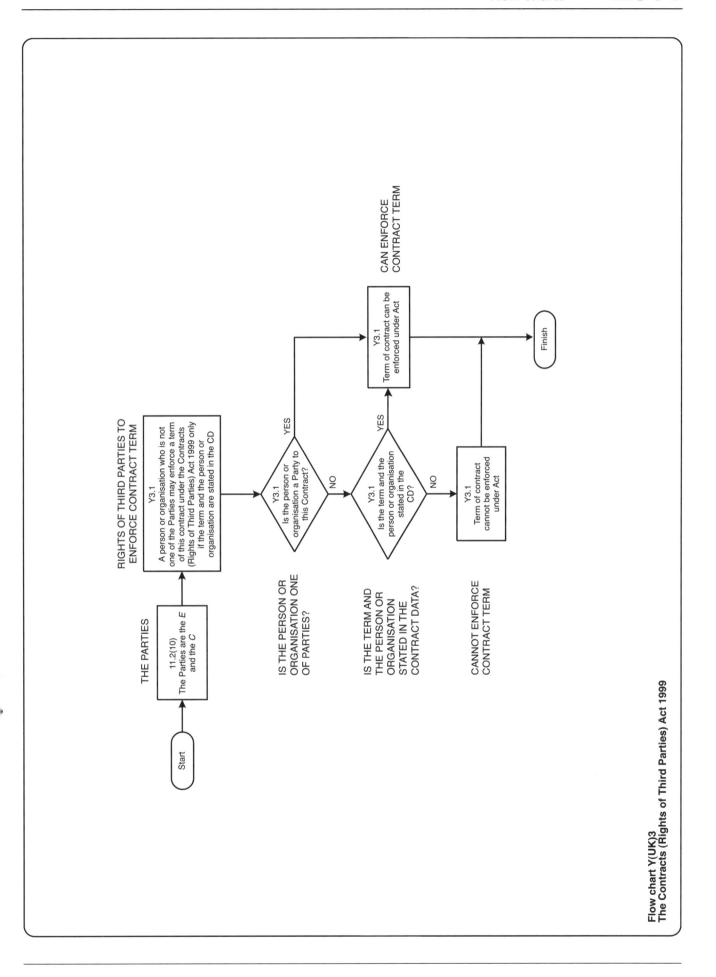

THE PARTIES

11.2(10)
The Parties are the *E* and the *C*

RIGHTS OF THIRD PARTIES TO ENFORCE CONTRACT TERM

Y3.1
A person or organisation who is not one of the Parties may enforce a term of this contract under the Contracts (Rights of Third Parties) Act 1999 only if the term and the person or organisation are stated in the CD

Start

IS THE PERSON OR ORGANISATION ONE OF PARTIES?

Y3.1
Is the person or organisation a Party to this Contract?

YES

NO

IS THE TERM AND THE PERSON OR ORGANISATION STATED IN THE CONTRACT DATA?

Y3.1
Is the term and the person or organisation stated in the CD?

YES

NO

CANNOT ENFORCE CONTRACT TERM

Y3.1
Term of contract cannot be enforced under Act

CAN ENFORCE CONTRACT TERM

Y3.1
Term of contract can be enforced under Act

Finish

Flow chart Y(UK)3
The Contracts (Rights of Third Parties) Act 1999